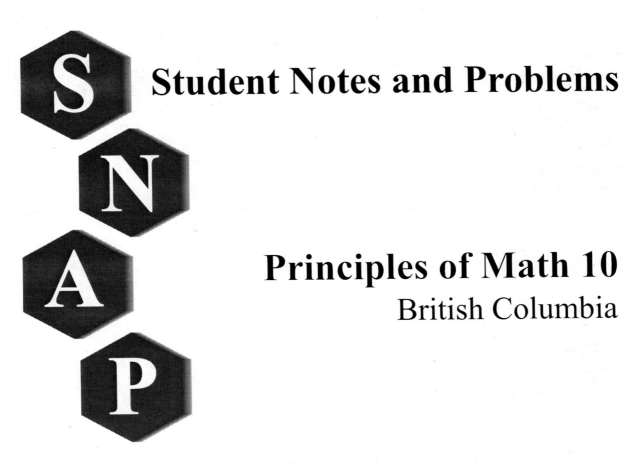

Student Notes and Problems

Principles of Math 10
British Columbia

CASTLE ROCK
RESEARCH CORP

Publisher
Gautam Rao

Contributor
Nadine Molnar
Rob Shkrobot
Krista Zirk

Rao, Gautam, 1961 –
STUDENT NOTES AND PROBLEMS – Principles of Math 10

1. Mathematics – Juvenile Literature. I. Title

Published by
Castle Rock Research Corp.
2340 Manulife Place
10180 – 101 Street
Edmonton, AB T5J 3S4

2 3 FP 10 09

Dedicated to the memory of Dr. V. S. Rao

STUDENT NOTES AND PROBLEMS WORKBOOKS

Student Notes and Problems (SNAP) workbooks are a series of support resources in mathematics for students in grades 3 to 12 and in science for students in grades 9 to 12. SNAP workbooks are 100% aligned with curriculum. The resources are designed to support classroom instructions and provide students with additional examples, practice exercises, and tests. SNAP workbooks are ideal for use all year long at school and at home.

The following is a summary of the key features of all SNAP workbooks.

UNIT OPENER PAGES

- summarize the curriculum outcomes addressed in the unit in age-appropriate language
- identify the lessons by title
- list the prerequisite knowledge and skills the student should know prior to beginning the unit

LESSONS

- provide essential teaching pieces and explanations of the concepts
- include example problems and questions with complete, detailed solutions that demonstrate the problem-solving process

NOTES BARS

- contain key definitions, formulas, reminders, and important steps or procedures
- provide space for students to add their own notes and helpful reminders

PRACTICE EXERCISES

- include questions that relate to each of the curriculum outcomes for the unit
- provide practice in applying the lesson concepts

REVIEW SUMMARIES

- provide a succinct review of the key concepts in the unit

PRACTICE TESTS

- assess student learning of the unit concepts

ANSWERS AND SOLUTIONS

- demonstrate the step-by-step process or problem-solving method used to arrive at the correct answer

Answers and solutions are provided in each workbook for the odd-numbered questions. A *SNAP Solutions Manual* that contains answers and complete solutions for all questions is also available.

CONTENTS

Exponents and Radicals

Line Segments and Graphs

Functions and Relations

Answers and Solutions

NOTES

TRIGONOMETRY

When you are finished this unit, you should be able to . . .

- solve problems involving two right triangles in 2-D and 3-D applications
- determine the value of angles from 0° to 180° by using the Sine and Cosine ratios
- apply the Sine Law to solve problems
- apply the Cosine Law to solve problems

PREREQUISITE SKILLS AND KNOWLEDGE

Prior to beginning this unit, you should be able to . . .

- identify Sine, Cosine, and Tangent ratios
- solve simple algebraic equations
- isolate variables in algebraic expressions
- translate word problems into diagrams
- translate word problems into algebraic expressions

Lesson 1 SINE, COSINE, AND TANGENT RATIOS

NOTES

This chapter will focus on questions involving the primary trigonometric ratios of sine, cosine, and tangent. However, since it is common for trigonometry questions to involve other procedures that are part of previous courses, it is helpful to review these first.

PYTHAGOREAN THEOREM

In any right-angle triangle, the square of the hypotenuse is equal to the sum of the squares of the other two sides.

Vertices are labelled with a capital letter and the side opposite is labelled with a lower case letter.

This can be illustrated as

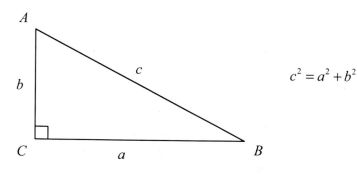

$$c^2 = a^2 + b^2$$

Example 1

Find the length of the unknown side.

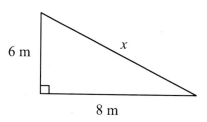

Solution

$$c^2 = a^2 + b^2$$

Substitute the given values into this formula:

$$x^2 = 6^2 + 8^2$$

$$x^2 = 36 + 64$$

$$x^2 = 100$$

$$x = \sqrt{100}$$

$$x = 10 \text{ m}$$

Remember that the hypotenuse is the largest side. It is across from the right angle and is normally identified by the letter c.

The unknown side has a length of 10 m.

SUM OF THE ANGLES IN A TRIANGLE

In any triangle, the sum of the three angles is always equal to 180°. For example:

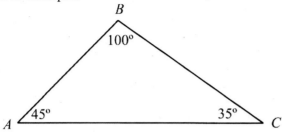

$$\angle A + \angle B + \angle C = 180°$$
$$45° + 100° + 35° = 180°$$
$$180° = 180°$$

Angles are commonly labelled with uppercase letters such as A, B, or C. It is common to represent unknown angles with Greek letters such as θ (theta), α (alpha), and ϕ (phi).

Example 2

a) Find the measure of the unknown angle.

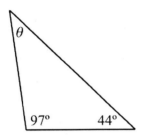

An acute angle is an angle that measures less than 90°.

Solution

$$\theta + 97° + 44° = 180°$$
$$\theta + 141° = 180°$$
$$\theta = 39°$$

b) Determine the measure of $\angle XYZ$.

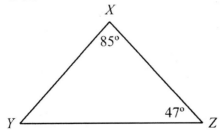

When the name of an angle is given as three letters, the angle represented by the middle letter is required.

Solution

$$y + 85° + 47° = 180°$$
$$y + 132° = 180°$$
$$y = 48°$$

NOTES

SINE, COSINE, AND TANGENT

The three primary trigonometric ratios describe the ratios of the different sides in a right-angled triangle.

These ratios always use one of the acute angles as a point of reference. The 90° angle is never used. In the illustration that follows, the ratios are described relative to angle θ.

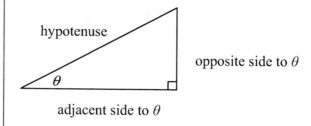

$$\sin \theta = \frac{\text{opposite}}{\text{hypotenuse}} \qquad \cos \theta = \frac{\text{adjacent}}{\text{hypotenuse}}$$

$$\tan \theta = \frac{\text{opposite}}{\text{adjacent}}$$

Example 3

Provide the three primary trigonometric ratios for α.

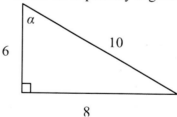

Solution

First, identify the sides relative to α.

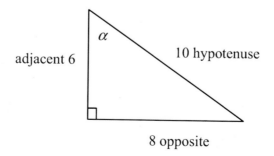

Next, state the ratios and reduce them to their lowest terms.

$$\sin \alpha = \frac{8}{10} = \frac{4}{5}$$

$$\cos \alpha = \frac{6}{10} = \frac{3}{5}$$

$$\tan \alpha = \frac{8}{6} = \frac{4}{3}$$

UNKNOWN SIDE

A common use of the trigonometric ratios is to find the value of an unknown side or angle in a triangle.

In order to find an unknown side using trigonometric ratios, the length of one other side and the measure of one of the acute angles is needed.

Example 4

Find the length of the unknown side to the nearest tenth of a centimetre.

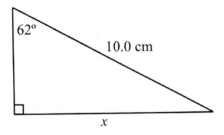

Solution

First, identify the known and desired sides of the triangle relative to the acute angle that is known and will be used in the calculation.

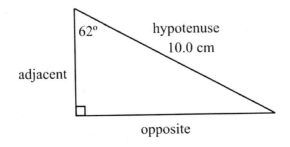

Your calculator must be in degree mode when solving trigonometric problems.

Always start with the angle that is given, then label the opposite and adjacent sides.

Since we know the length of the hypotenuse, and as we are trying to find the opposite side, we need to use sine.

$$\sin 62° = \frac{x}{10}$$

$$10 \sin 62° = x$$

$$x \approx 8.8 \text{ cm}$$

Example 5

Find the length of the unknown side to the nearest tenth of a metre.

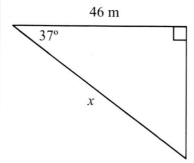

Solution

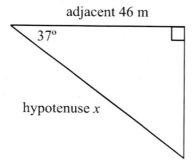

$$\cos 37° = \frac{46}{x}$$

$$x \cos 37° = 46$$

$$x = \frac{46}{\cos 37°}$$

$$x \approx 57.6 \text{ m}$$

UNKNOWN ANGLE

In order to find an unknown angle in a right triangle, the lengths of two of the three sides must be known.

Example 6

Find the indicated angle to the nearest tenth of a metre.

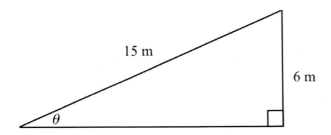

Solution

Label the given sides relative to the angle that you are trying to determine.

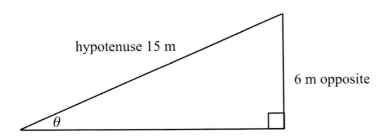

Since the opposite side and hypotenuse are known, we use the sine ratios:

$$\sin\theta = \frac{6}{15}$$

To solve for θ, we take the inverse sine of both sides:

$$\theta = \sin^{-1}\left(\frac{6}{15}\right)$$
$$\theta \approx 23.6°$$

Example 7

Determine the measure of the unknown angle.

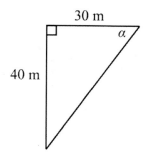

Solution

Label the given sides.

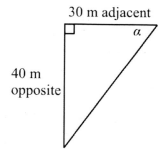

Since the adjacent and opposite sides are known, the tangent ratio is used.

$$\tan \alpha = \frac{40}{30}$$

$$\alpha = \tan^{-1}\left(\frac{40}{30}\right)$$
$$\alpha \approx 53.1°$$

Often, it is desirable to find all the unknown sides and angles of a triangle. This is referred to as solving the triangle.

In order to solve a triangle, it is common to use the Pythagorean theorem, the rule that the sum of the angles in a triangle equals 180°, and the trigonometric ratios.

Example 8

Solve the following triangle.

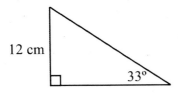

Solution

If it has not already been done for you, it is helpful to label the unknowns that you are trying to find.

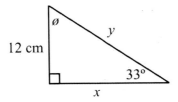

The measure of ϕ can be determined first.

$$90° + 33° + \phi = 180°$$
$$\phi = 57°$$

Next, the length of x can be calculated.

$$\tan 33° = \frac{12}{x}$$
$$x \tan 33° = 12$$
$$x = \frac{12}{\tan 33°}$$
$$x \approx 18.5 \text{ cm}$$

The final side, y, can be determined either by using the Pythagorean theorem or by using trigonometric ratios.

Using the Pythagorean theorem:

$$c^2 = a^2 + b^2$$
$$y^2 = 12^2 + x^2$$

NOTES

On some graphing calculators, you can use the key "2ⁿᵈ Ans" rather than type $\left(\dfrac{12}{\tan 33}\right)$ again.

When substituting for x, it is best to use the exact value, $\dfrac{12}{\tan 33°}$, rather than the approximate value of 18.5 cm.

$$y^2 = 12^2 + \left(\frac{12}{\tan 33°}\right)^2$$

$$y = \sqrt{12^2 + \left(\frac{12}{\tan 33°}\right)^2}$$

$$y \approx 22.0 \text{ cm}$$

Using the sine ratio:

$$\sin 33° = \frac{12}{y}$$

$$y \sin 33° = 12$$

$$y = \frac{12}{\sin 33°}$$

$$y \approx 22.0 \text{ cm}$$

The value of y is the same when using either the Pythagorean theorem or trigonometric ratios.

PRACTICE EXERCISES

1. Which of the following triangles provide enough information with which to solve the triangle?

   Do not actually solve the triangles.

   a)

   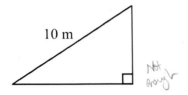

   10 m

   Not enough

   b)

   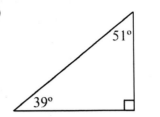

   51°

   39°

   enough

   c)

   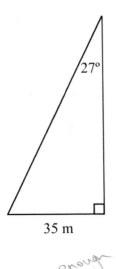

   27°

   35 m

   enough

   d)

   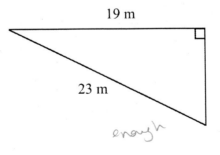

   19 m

   23 m

   enough

2. In order to find the value of θ in the triangle below, which trigonometric ratio would you use?

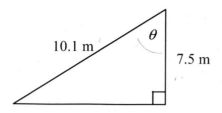

    A. Sine
    B. Cosine
    C. Tangent
    D. There is not enough information to determine θ.

3. Find the length of the unknown side labelled x.

    a)

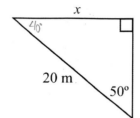

$\angle 40°$

$\cos 40° = \dfrac{x}{20} \times 20 = 15.3$

    b)

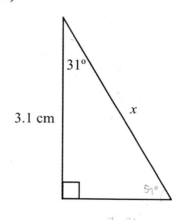

$\cos(31) = \dfrac{31}{x}$

$\dfrac{\cos(31)x}{\cos(31)} = \dfrac{3.1}{\cos(31)}$

$x = 3.6\,cm$

4. Determine the measure of the indicated unknown angles.

a)

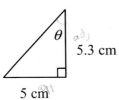

θ
ad)
5.3 cm

5 cm

$$\tan^{-1}\left(\frac{5}{5.3}\right) = 43°$$

b)

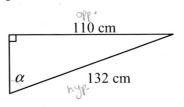

opp'
110 cm

α
hyp.
132 cm

$$\sin^{-1}\left(\frac{110}{132}\right) = 56°$$

5. Solve the following triangles.

a)

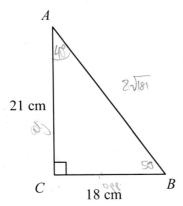

A

40

21 cm

$2\sqrt{181}$

adj

C
18 cm
opp
B
50

$$21^2 + 18^2 = c^2$$
$$\sqrt{c^2} = \sqrt{724}$$
$$c = 2\sqrt{181}$$
$$c = 27 cm$$

∠A
$$\tan^{-1} = \left(\frac{18}{21}\right)$$
$$∠A = 40$$

b)

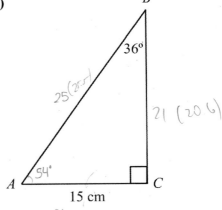

B

36°

25 (25.5)

21 (20.6)

A
54°
15 cm
C

∠A

$$\sin 36 = \frac{15}{x}$$
$$\frac{x\sin(36)}{\sin 36} = \frac{15}{\sin 36}$$
$$x = 25 (25.5)$$
$$15^2 + b^2 = 25.5^2$$
$$-15^2 \qquad -15^2$$
$$\sqrt{b^2} = \sqrt{425.25}$$
$$b = 21$$

Lesson 2 PROBLEMS INVOLVING TWO RIGHT TRIANGLES

NOTES

Many trigonometry questions require more than a single calculation in order to find the desired information. In some questions, the order of these calculations is unimportant, while in others, the order is crucial to determine the unknown values.

Example 1

Find the value of x.

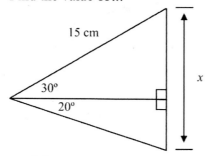

Solution

In order to find the entire length of x, the question must be broken down into two separate calculations. First, label (assign variables) the first lengths that will be found.

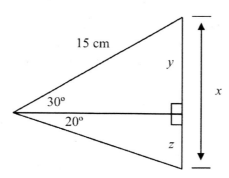

Since x cannot be calculated directly, calculate y and z instead, and then add them.

$x = y + z$

It does not matter which length, y or z, is calculated first. Using the tangent ratio:

$\tan 30° = \dfrac{y}{15}$

$y = 15 \tan 30°$

$y \approx 8.7$ cm

$\tan 20° = \dfrac{z}{15}$

$z = 15 \tan 20°$

$z \approx 5.5$ cm

So,
$x = y + z$

In order to avoid rounding errors, the expressions for y and z can be substituted into the question. This way, the only rounding will be at the end of the question.

$x = 15 \tan 30° + 15 \tan 20°$

$x \approx 14.11$ cm

Example 2

Find the value of x.

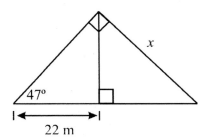

Solution

Start by filling in any of the values that you can determine easily by knowing that the three angles in a triangle total 180°.

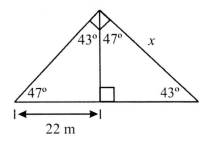

Since we do not know the length of any sides of the triangle that x is a part of, the first step is to determine one such side.

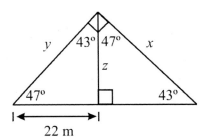

NOTES

Either y or z will allow us to calculate x. For no particular reason, z will be chosen.

Using the tangent ratio:

$$\tan 47° = \frac{z}{22}$$
$$22\tan 47° = z$$
$$z \approx 23.6$$

Now, x can be determined using z, or the expression for z.

$$\sin 43° = \frac{z}{x}$$
$$x\sin 43° = z$$

$$x = \frac{z}{\sin 43°}$$

$$x = \frac{22\tan 47°}{\sin 43°}$$

$$x \approx 34.6$$

Many of these questions take the form of word problems or applications. In this type of question, it is very important to sketch the correct diagram. Knowledge of some key phrases will help ensure that diagrams are correctly sketched.

ANGLE OF ELEVATION

Angles are formed by two rays that have a common starting point. An angle of elevation is measured between two such rays, where one of the rays is horizontal and the other is above this horizontal ray, as illustrated below.

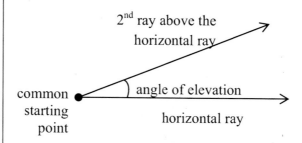

ANGLE OF DEPRESSION

An angle of depression is similar to any angle of elevation. However, the second angle is below the horizontal heading downward, as shown below.

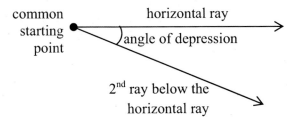

Example 3

State whether each angle in the following triangles is an angle of elevation, depression, or neither.

a)   **b)**

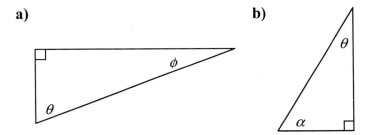

Solution

a) θ is neither an angle of elevation nor depression. Neither of the sides of the triangle that form angle θ is horizontal.

ϕ is an angle of depression.

b) θ is neither.

α is an angle of elevation.

Example 4

Sketch a diagram for each of the following scenarios involving angles of depression and elevation.

a) A cat watches a bird in a tree. The bird is at an angle of elevation of 40° from the cat.

b) From the top of a cliff, an observer watches a boat on the ocean. The angle of depression from the observer to the boat is 15°.

Solution

a)

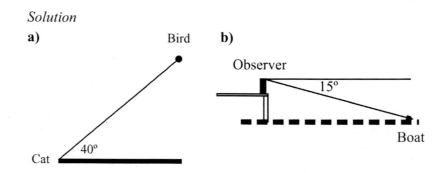

Example 5

The cat in Example 4 is still watching the bird in the tree. The bird remains at an angle of elevation of 40°. If the cat is 7.1 m from the base of the tree, how high up in the tree is the bird?

It is a common and acceptable assumption that trees, buildings, light posts, etc., are perpendicular to the ground.

Solution

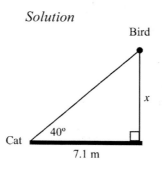

$$\tan 40° = \frac{x}{7.1}$$
$$x = 7.1 \tan 40°$$
$$x \approx 6.0 \text{ m}$$

Example 6

Lexi is standing in her yard. She sees a cat sitting directly west of her. Directly east of her is a dog. Lexi's eye level is 1.48 m high. To look directly at where the cat is sitting, she looks down at an angle of depression of 30°. To the dog, the angle of depression is 25°. How far apart are the cat and dog?

Solution

First, sketch and label a diagram:

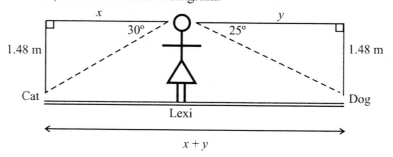

Notice that $x + y$ at eye level will be the same as $x + y$ on the ground.

The distance between the cat and dog $= x + y$.

$$\tan 30° = \frac{1.48}{x}$$

$$x = \frac{1.48}{\tan 30°}$$

$$\tan 25° = \frac{1.48}{y}$$

$$y = \frac{1.48}{\tan 25°}$$

distance $= x + y$

$$= \frac{1.48}{\tan 30°} + \frac{1.48}{\tan 25°}$$

$$\approx 5.74 \text{ m}$$

Example 7

Stephen is standing on the street, 20 m from the base of a tall office building. He is looking up at his friend David at an angle of elevation of 27°. His friend Amorita is higher up, at an angle of elevation of 50°. How much higher up is Amorita?

Solution
First, sketch a diagram:

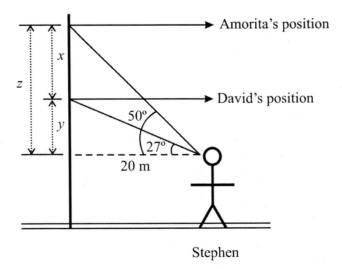

Stephen

The difference between David's and Amorita's position is represented by x. To find x, find z and y and then subtract.

$$x = z - y$$

$$\tan 27° = \frac{y}{20}$$

$$y = 20 \tan 27°$$

$$\tan 50° = \frac{z}{20}$$
$$z = 20 \tan 50°$$

$$x = z - y$$
$$x = 20 \tan 50° - 20 \tan 27°$$
$$x \approx 13.6 \text{ m}$$

Example 8

John took his pup tent on a camping trip. If one side of the tent measures 240 cm and forms a 55° angle with the ground, how tall is the tent?

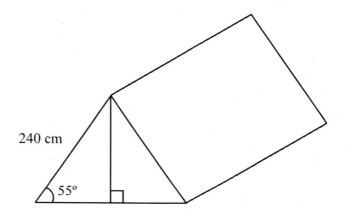

240 cm

55°

Solution

$$\sin 55° = \frac{x}{240}$$
$$x = 240 \sin 55°$$
$$x = 196.6 \text{ cm}$$

PRACTICE EXERCISES

1. In the following diagram, what angle is the angle of elevation?

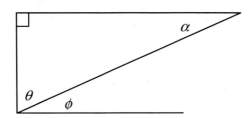

    A. α
    B. θ
    C. ϕ
    D. There is no angle of elevation.

2. In order to calculate the value of θ in the following diagram, you must first calculate
    A. z by using the cosine ratio
    B. x by using the sine ratio
    C. α by using the sum of the angles in a triangle
    D. y by using the tangent ratio

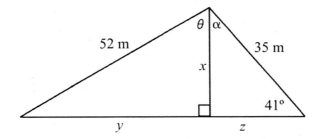

$s = \frac{o}{H}$

$180 - (90 + \tan^{-1}(\frac{20}{10}))$

3. Determine the unknown indicated sides or angles.

a)

26.56
10√5
65.43°
44.6 x
20 m
θ
90°
26.56
10 m   39.8

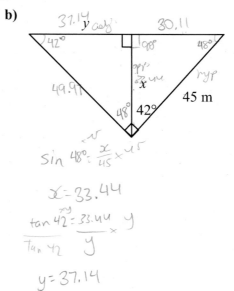

b)

37.14 y adj.   30.11
42°   90°   48°
49.9   99°
44
x
hyp
48° 42°   45 m

$20^2 + 10^2 = c^2$ $\theta = \tan^{-1}(\frac{20}{10})$

$c^2 = 500$

$c = 10\sqrt{5} \, (22.3)$ $\frac{\sin 26.6}{\sin 26.6} = \frac{20}{x}$

$\tan^{-1}(\frac{20}{10})$ $x = \frac{20}{\sin 26.6}$

$\tan^{-1}(2)$ $x = 44.6$

$\sin 48 = \frac{x}{45} \times 45$

$x = 33.44$

$\frac{\tan 42}{\tan 42} = \frac{33.44}{y} \times \frac{y}{x}$

$y = 37.14$

4. On a particular street, the streetlights are in a straight line, but they are not evenly spaced, as shown in the diagram below. From the top of streetlight *B* to the bottom of streetlight *A*, the angle of depression is 25°. The angle of depression from the top of streetlight *B* to the bottom of streetlight *C* is 22°. Each streetlight is 5.5 m tall. What is the distance between streetlight *A* and streetlight *C*?

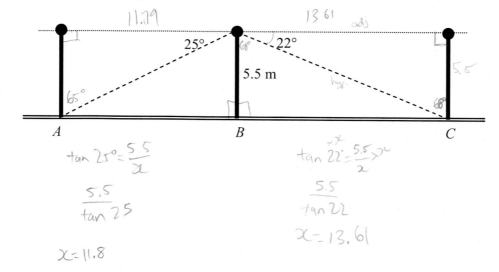

11.79   13.61 adj
25°   68° 22°
5.5 m
65°   68°
A   B   C

$\tan 25° = \frac{5.5}{x}$ $\tan 22° = \frac{5.5}{x}$

$\frac{5.5}{\tan 25}$ $\frac{5.5}{\tan 22}$

$x = 11.8$ $x = 13.61$

$11.79 + 13.61 = 25.4 \text{ m}$

5. A lighthouse attendant spots a ship due north at an angle of depression of 15°, and another ship that is due east at an angle of depression of 18°. If the lighthouse is 12 m high, how far apart are the ships?

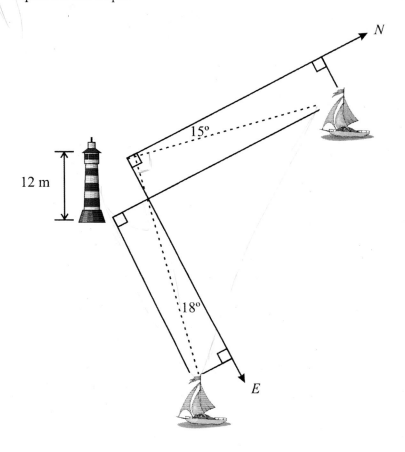

$$\text{Sin } 42 = \frac{x}{45} \times 45 \frac{.6691}{45} = 0.014 = 85\%$$

.6691

$$30.1 = \frac{x}{45}$$

Lesson 3 SINE AND COSINE FOR ANGLES FROM 0° TO 180°

NOTES

You may consider the 1ˢᵗ ray as the *x*-axis, and call it "the initial arm." The 2ⁿᵈ ray may be called "the rotational arm" because it rotates relative to the 1ˢᵗ ray.

Until now, the discussion of the sine and cosine of angles has been limited to acute angles. In this lesson, obtuse angles measuring between 90° and 180° will also be considered.

A helpful way to examine such angles is to use a coordinate plane. When graphing angles on the coordinate plane, think of the positive *x*-axis as one of the rays that forms the angle. Then, think of the second ray as being situated counterclockwise 0° to 180° from the first ray.

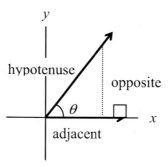

In order to determine the trigonometric ratios for θ, it is necessary to draw a vertical line from the 2ⁿᵈ ray to the *x*-axis. This allows for the ratios of the sides to be determined in a familiar way since the vertical forms a right angle with the *x*-axis.

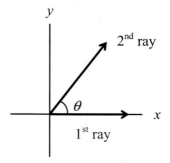

Consider an angle that has a second ray, or rotational arm, passing through the point (3, 4).

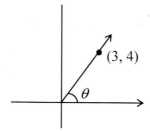

Draw a vertical line passing through this point.

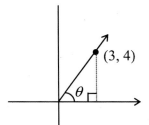

Label the lengths of the sides and use the Pythagorean theorem to find the length of the hypotenuse.

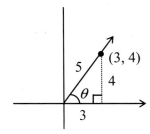

Now, state the sine and cosine ratios.

$$\sin\theta = \frac{4}{5} \qquad \text{and} \qquad \cos\theta = \frac{3}{5}$$

θ can now be determined.

$$\theta = \sin^{-1}\left(\frac{4}{5}\right) \qquad \text{and} \qquad \theta = \cos^{-1}\left(\frac{3}{5}\right)$$

$$\theta \approx 53.1° \qquad\qquad\qquad \theta \approx 53.1°$$

When moving from acute to obtuse angles, it becomes useful to think of the sides of a triangle as:

• the vertical distance from the *x*-axis
• the horizontal distance from the *y*-axis
• the length of the 2ⁿᵈ ray, or rotational arm from the origin to the point where the ray intersects the vertical lines

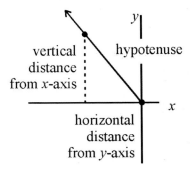

NOTES

α is measured from the positive *x*-axis to the ray that passes through the point (–3, 4).

Now, consider an obtuse angle, α, with the same vertical distance as our previous acute angle, θ, and an equal horizontal distance, but in the opposite direction.

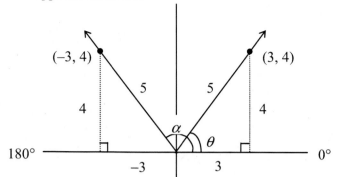

Because the vertical distance and the ray length are equal for θ and α, these two angles have the same sine ratio.

$$\sin \theta = \frac{4}{5} \qquad\qquad \sin \alpha = \frac{4}{5}$$

The cosines are not equal. One is positive and the other is negative.

$$\cos \theta = \frac{3}{5} \qquad\qquad \cos \alpha = -\frac{3}{5}$$

The relationship between these angles can be summarized as follows.

Two angles that add up to 180° are said to be supplementary.

When θ and α are angles between 0° and 180°:

$$\sin \theta = \sin \alpha \ \text{ if } \ \theta + \alpha = 180°$$

$$\cos \theta = -\cos \alpha \ \text{ if } \ \theta + \alpha = 180°$$

Example 1

Find the approximate values of the following sines and cosines.

a) $\sin 20°$ and $\sin 160°$
b) $\cos 72°$ and $\cos 108°$

Solution

a) Using a calculator:

$$\sin 20° \approx 0.342$$
Since $20° + 160° = 180°$,
$$\sin 160° = \sin 20°$$
$$\approx 0.342$$

b) Using a calculator:

$$\cos 72° \approx 0.309$$
Since $72° + 108° = 180°$,
$$\cos 108° = -\cos 72°$$
$$\approx -0.309$$

This information about obtuse angles can be used in reverse to determine the value of an angle when the angle's sine or cosine is known.

Since any angle and its compliment have the same sine ratio, questions that ask for an angle when a sine ratio is given will always have two answers.

Example 2

Determine the values of θ. Round to the nearest degree.

$$\sin \theta = 0.45$$

Solution
Using a calculator:

$$\theta = \sin^{-1}(0.45)$$
$$\approx 27°$$

This is only one angle, but both must be found.
The second angle will be supplementary to this one:

$$27° + \theta = 180°$$
$$\theta = 180° - 27°$$
$$\theta = 153°$$

NOTES

Example 3

Determine the values of θ in the following questions, where $0° \leq \theta \leq 180°$
(this means that θ is between 0° and 180°).

a) $\sin\theta = 0.22$

b) $\cos\theta = 0.15$

Solution

a) First angle:

$\theta = \sin^{-1}(0.22)$

$\quad = 12.7°$

Second angle:

$\theta = 180° - 12.7°$

$\quad = 167.3°$

b) Since this question gives a cosine ratio, there will be only one angle that θ can equal. (Note: the ratio is positive, so θ will be acute.)

using a calculator:

$\theta = \cos^{-1}(0.15)$

$\quad = 81.4°$

Another way to illustrate the values of $\sin\theta$ and $\cos\theta$, where $0° \leq \theta \leq 180°$, is by looking at the graphs of $y = \sin\theta$ and $y = \cos\theta$.

Example 4

a) Using a graphing calculator, graph $y = \sin\theta$ using the window settings

$X[0, 180, 10]$

$Y[0, 2, 1]$

b) Using the same window settings, graph $y = \cos\theta$.

Solution

a) On a graphing calculator, enter $\sin x$ into $y_1 =$. Notice that most graphing calculators use x instead of θ. This is not a problem.

Enter the window settings.
Press the Graph button.

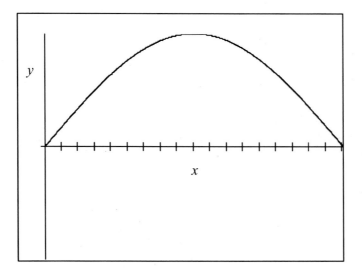

Notice that for every y-value, there are **two** x-values (θ-values). This supports the previous information that was illustrated regarding supplementary angles.

b) Enter $y = \cos\theta$ into $y_1 = $.

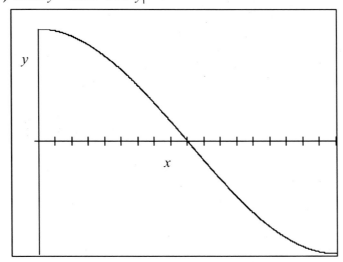

Notice that each y-value has only one x-value (θ-value).

PRACTICE EXERCISES

1. Which angle has the same sine ratio as $65°$?
   A. $-65°$
   B. $115°$
   C. $155°$
   D. There is no angle that has the same sine ratio as $65°$.

2. Find the sine and cosine ratio for each of the following angles.
   a) $10°$

      sin

   b) $95°$

   c) $170°$

3. Given the following ratios, determine the unknown angle(s), where $0° \leq \theta \leq 180°$.
   a) $\cos \theta = 0.5$ b) $\sin \theta = 0.5$

   c) $\cos \theta = -\dfrac{2}{3}$ d) $\sin \theta = \dfrac{1}{3}$

4. The angle $180° - \phi$ has the same sine ratio as the angle _____.

PRACTICE QUIZ

1. Use the diagram to fill in the blanks below.

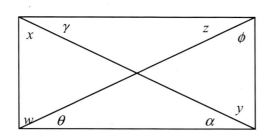

a) _____ *x* _____ and _____ *a* _____ are angles of elevation.

b) _____ *y* _____ and _____ *z* _____ are angles of depression.

2. Find the indicated unknown side length or angle. Round sides to the nearest tenth and angles to the nearest degree.

a)

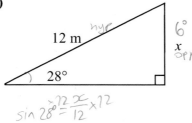

$$\sin 28° = \frac{x}{12} \times 12$$

$x = 5.6$

$x = 6°$

b)

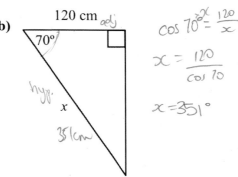

$$\cos 70° = \frac{120}{x} \rightarrow x$$

$$x = \frac{120}{\cos 70}$$

$$x = 351°$$

c)

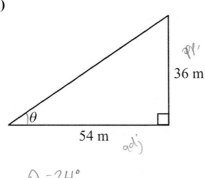

$\theta = 34°$

d)

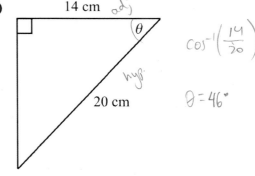

$$\cos^{-1}\left(\frac{14}{20}\right)$$

$$\theta = 46°$$

3. Find the value of θ for each of the following values, where $0 \leq \theta \leq 180°$.
Round your answers to the nearest degree.

    a) $\cos \theta = 0.223\,3$ **b)** $\sin \theta = 0.258\,9$

Lesson 4   THE SINE LAW

Many triangles do not contain right angles. With such triangles, the primary trigonometric ratios cannot be used. New methods must be developed in order to solve such triangles.

In the Sine Law, the primary trigonometric ratios are used to develop a new method.

Consider the acute triangle $\triangle ABC$ below.

NOTES

An acute triangle has three acute angles.

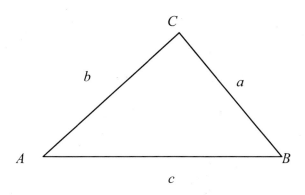

In order to find a connection with right triangles, draw a line from C perpendicular to AB. Since this line represents the height, call it h.

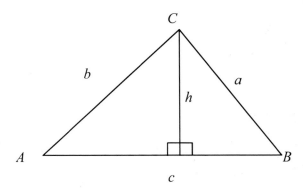

There are now two right triangles. Using the primary trigonometric ratios,

$$\sin A = \frac{h}{b} \qquad \text{and} \qquad \sin B = \frac{h}{a}$$

Solving for h in each case,

$$h = b\sin A \qquad \text{and} \qquad h = a\sin B$$

Since $h = h$, $b\sin A = a\sin B$.

Isolate the angle on each side by dividing both sides by ab.

NOTES

$$\frac{b\sin A}{ab} = \frac{a\sin B}{ab}$$

$$\frac{\sin A}{a} = \frac{\sin B}{b}$$

Only use two ratios at a time. Therefore, you need to have one unknown and three known quantities.

The same procedure can be used with C and either A or B, which leads to the Sine Law.

$$\frac{\sin A}{a} = \frac{\sin B}{b} = \frac{\sin C}{c}$$

This is sometimes written as:

$$\frac{a}{\sin A} = \frac{b}{\sin B} = \frac{c}{\sin C}$$

The Sine Law can be used to find unknown sides or angles in non-right triangles provided enough information is known about the other sides and angles.

Consider the following triangle.

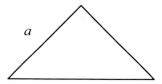

In order to determine the length of a, you must be given all of the following information:

- the opposite angle to a
- another complete angle/side pair

Either of the following triangles gives enough information to determine the length of side a.

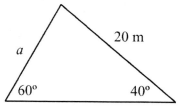

- The opposite angle to a: 40°
- The complete angle/side pair: 60°/20 m

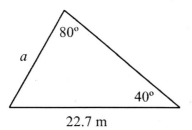

22.7 m

- The opposite angle to *a*: 40°
- The complete angle/side pair: 80°/22.7 m

In order to solve one of these questions, it is very helpful to label the triangle.

Consider the first of the two triangles above:

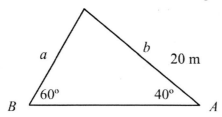

Now, substitute into the Sine Law:

$$\frac{\sin A}{a} = \frac{\sin B}{b}$$

$$\frac{\sin 40°}{a} = \frac{\sin 60°}{20}$$

or

$$\frac{a}{\sin A} = \frac{b}{\sin B}$$

$$\frac{a}{\sin 40} = \frac{20}{\sin 60}$$

$$a = \frac{20 \sin 40}{\sin 60}$$

$$\approx 14.8 \text{ m}$$

Solve for *a*:

$$20 \sin 40° = a \sin 60°$$

$$\frac{20 \sin 40°}{\sin 60°} = a$$

$$a \approx 14.8 \text{ m}$$

To make solving easier, it is helpful to have the unknown in the numerator, so use either one of the Sine Law methods. This way, you only need to cross-multiply in one direction.

NOTES

NOTES

Example 1

Determine the value of x.

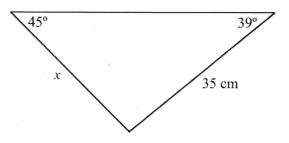

Solution

First label the diagram. The letters a, b, A, and B can be used for labelling.

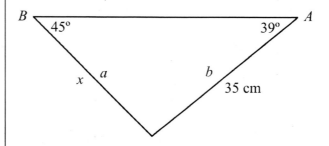

Substitute into the Sine Law:

$$\frac{\sin A}{a} = \frac{\sin B}{b}$$

$$\frac{\sin 39°}{x} = \frac{\sin 45°}{35}$$

Solve for x:

$$35 \sin 39° = x \sin 45°$$

$$\frac{35 \sin 39°}{\sin 45°} = x$$

$$x \approx 31.1 \, \text{cm}$$

The Sine Law can also be used to determine an unknown angle. In this type of question, the following information is required:

- the side opposite the unknown angle
- another complete angle/side pair

Example 2

Determine the indicated unknown angle.

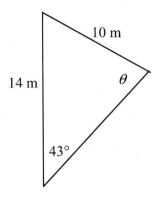

Solution

Label the diagram:

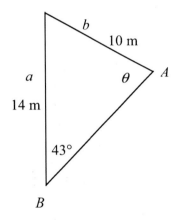

Substitute into the Sine Law:

$$\frac{\sin A}{a} = \frac{\sin B}{b}$$

$$\frac{\sin \theta}{14} = \frac{\sin 43°}{10}$$

Solve for θ:

$$\sin \theta = \frac{14 \sin 43°}{10}$$

$$\theta = \sin^{-1}\left(\frac{14 \sin 43°}{10}\right)$$

$$\theta \approx 72.7°$$

Remember to use the inverse function on your calculator to determine the angle.

PRACTICE EXERCISES

1. Which of the following ratios is correctly set up to solve for the unknown side length in the given triangle?

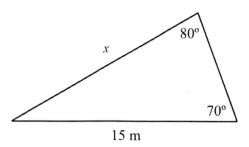

A. $\dfrac{\sin 80°}{x} = \dfrac{\sin 70°}{15}$

B. $\dfrac{\sin x}{70°} = \dfrac{\sin 15}{80°}$

C. $\dfrac{\sin 70°}{x} = \dfrac{\sin 80°}{15}$

D. $\dfrac{\sin x}{80°} = \dfrac{\sin 15}{70°}$

2. Find the indicated side length for each triangle.

a)

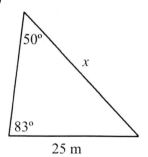

b)

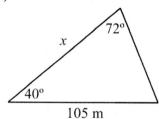

3. Find the indicated angle for each triangle and round to the nearest degree.

a)

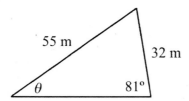

b)

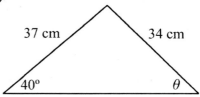

4. Find the unknown side length and angle.

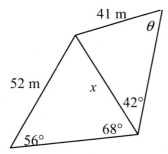

5. Determine the length of *XZ*.

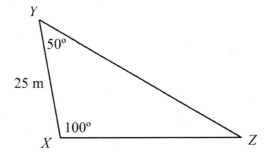

Lesson 5   THE COSINE LAW

When solving a triangle that is not a right triangle and cannot be solved using the Sine Law, it is possible to solve it using the Cosine Law.

The law is developed as follows.

Consider the following triangle:

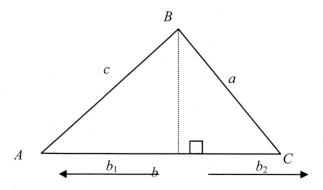

$\sin A = \dfrac{\text{altitude}}{c}$

So, altitude $= c \sin A$

$\cos A = \dfrac{b_1}{c}$, so

$b_1 = c \cos A$

$b_2 = b - b_1$

$\quad = b - c \cos A$

Using right-angle trigonometry, the altitude can be expressed as $c \sin A$ and the base can be divided into two parts: $(c \cos A)$ and $(b - c \cos A)$.

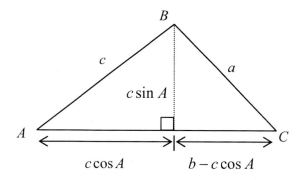

Using the triangle on the right and the Pythagorean theorem, we can write

$$a^2 = (b - c \cos A)^2 + (c \sin A)^2$$
$$a^2 = b^2 - 2bc \cos A + (c \cos A)^2 + (c \sin A)^2$$
$$a^2 = b^2 - 2bc \cos A + c^2 \cos^2 A + c^2 \sin^2 A$$
$$a^2 = b^2 - 2bc \cos A + c^2 (\cos^2 A + \sin^2 A)$$

For any angle A,

$$\cos^2 A + \sin^2 A = 1$$

We can make this substitution:

$$a^2 = b^2 - 2bc\cos A + c^2 \ (1)$$

Rearranging, we get

$$a^2 = b^2 + c^2 - 2bc\cos A$$

Using this form of the Cosine Law, an unknown side can be found if the angle opposite the unknown side is known and the other two sides are known.

Example 1

Find the length of the unknown side.

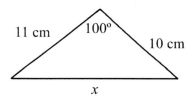

Solution

$$a^2 = b^2 + c^2 - 2bc\cos A$$

Substitute values and unknowns into the Cosine Law equation:

$$x^2 = 11^2 + 10^2 - 2(11)(10)\cos 100°$$

$$x = \sqrt{11^2 + 10^2 - 2(11)(10)\cos 100°}$$

$$x \approx 16.1\,\text{cm}$$

It is extremely important for the triangle's angles and opposite sides to be represented by the same letters (uppercase for angles and lowercase for the sides).

Note that you cannot use sine, cosine, or tangent ratios since this is not a right triangle. The Sine Law cannot be used since we do not have a complete set (angle and opposite side).

Note that in this triangle, we know a side, a contained angle, and another side. This is known as SAS (side-angle-side).

NOTES

Example 2

Find the unknown side.

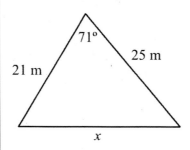

Solution

$a^2 = b^2 + c^2 - 2bc\cos A$

$x^2 = 25^2 + 21^2 - 2(25)(21)\cos 71°$

$x = \sqrt{25^2 + 21^2 - 2(25)(21)\cos 71°}$

$x \approx 26.9 \text{ m}$

The Cosine Law can also be rearranged in order to find an unknown angle.

$\cos A = \dfrac{b^2 + c^2 - a^2}{2bc}$

To find an angle using the Cosine Law, you must know all 3 sides, or SSS (side-side-side).

This formula can be used to find an unknown angle **only** if the lengths of all three sides are known.

Example 3

Find the indicated unknown angle.

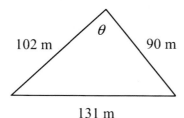

Solution

Since θ is the angle that we are trying to determine, it becomes $\angle A$, and 131 m becomes side a. Sides b and c are interchangeable.

$$\cos A = \frac{b^2 + c^2 - a^2}{2bc}$$

$$\cos \theta = \frac{102^2 + 90^2 - 131^2}{2(102)(90)}$$

$$\theta = \cos^{-1}\left(\frac{102^2 + 90^2 - 131^2}{2(102)(90)}\right)$$

$$\theta \approx 85.8°$$

Example 4

Find all the angles in the triangle below.

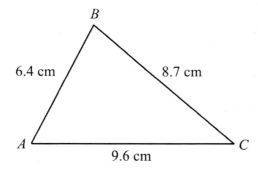

Solution

First, the Cosine Law should be used to determine any of the unknown angles.

$\angle A$ will be found first.

$$\cos A = \frac{b^2 + c^2 - a^2}{2bc}$$

$$\cos A = \frac{(9.6)^2 + (6.4)^2 - (8.7)^2}{2(9.6)(6.4)}$$

$$A = \cos^{-1}\left(\frac{(9.6)^2 + (6.4)^2 - (8.7)^2}{2(9.6)(6.4)}\right)$$

$$A \approx 62.136\ 5°$$

NOTES

When using previously calculated values, rounding should be kept to a minimum.

If using a graphing calculator, use the "2nd Ans" key to use the value prior to rounding.

Now that one angle/side pair is known, the Sine Law can be used to determine both of the other angles.

It should be noted that the Cosine Law could be used again instead of the Sine Law. The Sine Law was chosen because it requires slightly less work.

$$\frac{\sin A}{a} = \frac{\sin B}{b}$$

$$\frac{\sin(62.136\ 5°)}{8.7} = \frac{\sin B}{9.6}$$

$$\frac{9.6\sin(62.136\ 5°)}{8.7} = \sin B$$

$$B = \sin^{-1}\left(\frac{9.6\sin(62.136\ 5°)}{8.7}\right)$$

$$B \approx 77.295\ 8°$$

$$\frac{\sin A}{a} = \frac{\sin C}{c}$$

$$\frac{\sin(62.136\ 5°)}{8.7} = \frac{\sin C}{6.4}$$

$$\frac{6.4\sin(62.136\ 5°)}{8.7} = \sin C$$

$$C = \sin^{-1}\left(\frac{6.4\sin(62.136\ 5°)}{8.7}\right)$$

$$C \approx 40.567\ 7°$$

or

To find the last angle, subtract $\angle A$ and $\angle B$ from 180º.

The angles are $A \approx 62.1°$, $B \approx 77.3°$, and $C \approx 40.6°$.

PRACTICE EXERCISES

1. For each of the following questions, state whether the Sine Law or the Cosine Law should be used to determine the indicated side or angle. Do not solve the triangles.

   a)

   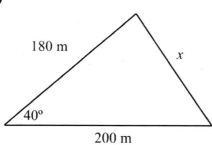

   b)

   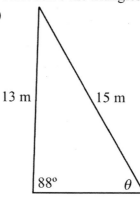

   c)

   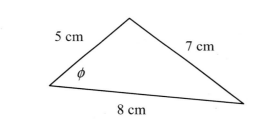

   d)

   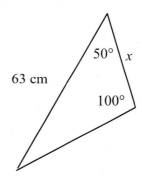

2. For each of the following triangles, determine the length of the unknown side.

   a)

   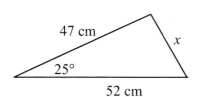

   b)

   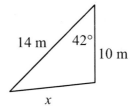

45

3. For each of the following triangles, determine the unknown angle indicated.

a)

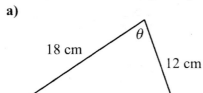

b)

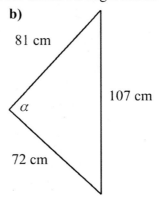

4. Which of the following ratios correctly uses the Cosine Law for the triangle given below?

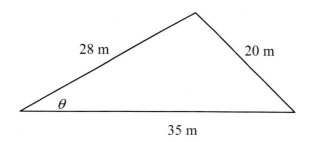

A. $\cos\theta = \dfrac{28^2 + 35^2 - 20^2}{2(28)(35)}$

B. $\cos\theta = \dfrac{20^2 + 28^2 - 35^2}{2(20)(28)}$

C. $\cos\theta = \dfrac{20^2 + 35^2 - 28^2}{2(20)(35)}$

D. $\cos\theta = \dfrac{28^2 + 35^2 - 20^2}{2(28)(20)}$

Lesson 6   MIXED PROBLEMS

Many questions require a combination of approaches.
The questions may involve two or three dimensions and may
require right-angle trigonometry equations combined with the Sine
and Cosine laws.

With these problems, it is important to:

1. have a clearly labelled diagram

2. avoid or minimize rounding until the last step

Example 1

a)   Determine the length of side x.

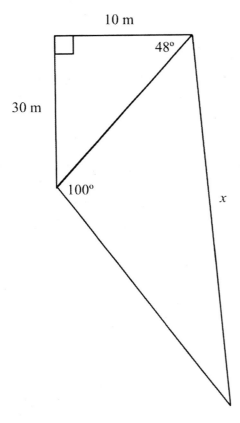

Solution

The Cosine Law can be used to find *x*, but only after another unknown side, now labelled *y*, is determined.

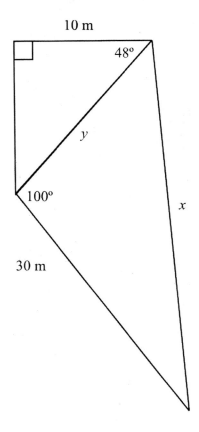

The cosine ratio can be used to find *y* in the smaller right angle.

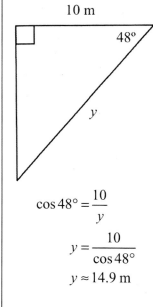

$$\cos 48° = \frac{10}{y}$$

$$y = \frac{10}{\cos 48°}$$

$$y \approx 14.9 \text{ m}$$

Next, use the calculated value for *y*, or even better, the expression for *y*, along with the Cosine Law to determine *x*.

$$a^2 = b^2 + c^2 - 2bc \cos A$$

$$x^2 = y^2 + 30^2 - 2y(30)\cos 100°$$

$$x^2 = \left(\frac{10}{\cos 48°}\right)^2 + 30^2 - 2\left(\frac{10}{\cos 48°}\right)(30)\cos 100°$$

$$x = \sqrt{\left(\frac{10}{\cos 48°}\right)^2 + 30^2 - 2\left(\frac{10}{\cos 48°}\right)(30)\cos 100°}$$

$$x \approx 35.8 \text{ m}$$

Example 2

A student standing a number of metres from the base of a building measures the angle of elevation to the tenth floor to be 50°.
The angle of elevation to the sixteenth floor is measured to be 60°.
The distance between the tenth and sixteenth floors is 15 m.
How far is the student from the base of the building?

Solution
First, sketch a diagram.

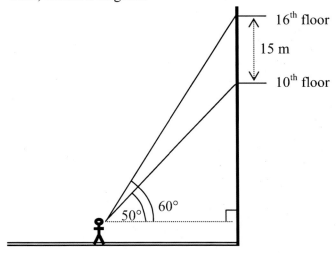

16th floor

15 m

10th floor

60°

50°

Label the given measurements and those that can easily be determined using the knowledge that the sum of the angles in a triangle is 180°.

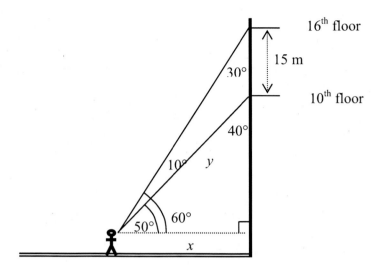

x can be found using the cosine ratio if y is determined first using the Sine Law.

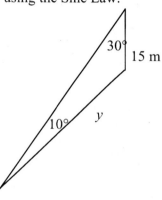

$$\frac{\sin 10°}{15} = \frac{\sin 30°}{y}$$

$$y = \frac{15 \sin 30°}{\sin 10°}$$

$$y \approx 43.2 \text{ m}$$

Now, use the cosine ratio:

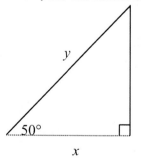

$$\cos 50° = \frac{x}{y}$$

$$\cos 50° = \frac{x}{\left(\dfrac{15 \sin 30°}{\sin 10°}\right)}$$

$$x = \cos 50° \left(\frac{15 \sin 30°}{\sin 10°}\right)$$

$$x \approx 27.8 \text{ m}$$

The student is standing 27.8 m from the building.

Example 3

A child is flying two kites as illustrated below.

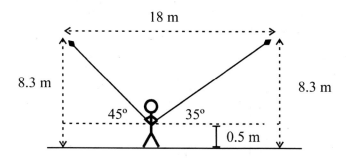

Both kites are 8.3 m above the ground, and the child is holding the kite strings 0.5 m off the ground. One kite string is at an angle of elevation of 35°, and the other is at an angle of elevation of 45°. One kite is flying to the child's right and the other is to the child's left. The kites are 18 m apart. What is the angle formed by the two kite strings?

Solution

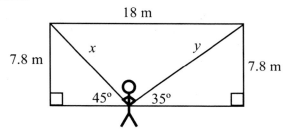

$$\sin 45° = \frac{7.8}{x}$$

$$x = \frac{7.8}{\sin 45°}$$

$$x \approx 11.0 \text{ m}$$

$$\sin 35° = \frac{7.8}{y}$$

$$y = \frac{7.8}{\sin 35°}$$

$$y \approx 13.6 \text{ m}$$

Now, the Cosine Law can be used to determine the angle:

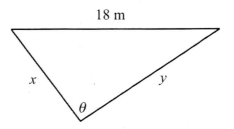

$$\cos A = \frac{b^2 + c^2 - a^2}{2bc}$$

$$\cos \theta = \frac{x^2 + y^2 - 18^2}{2xy}$$

$$\theta = \cos^{-1}\left(\frac{\left(\dfrac{7.8}{\sin 45°}\right)^2 + \left(\dfrac{7.8}{\sin 35°}\right)^2 - 18^2}{2\left(\dfrac{7.8}{\sin 45°}\right)\left(\dfrac{7.8}{\sin 35°}\right)}\right)$$

$$\theta \approx 93.3°$$

PRACTICE EXERCISES

1. Determine the lengths of the indicated sides.

a)

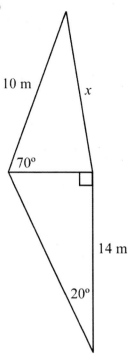

10 m

x

70°

14 m

20°

b)

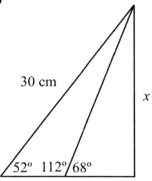

30 cm

x

52° 112° 68°

2. Determine the measure of the indicated angles.

a)

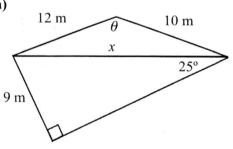

12 m   θ   10 m

x

25°

9 m

b)

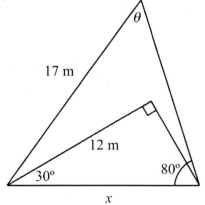

θ

17 m

12 m

30°

80°

x

53

3. The following diagram is in three dimensions. Determine the indicated side length.

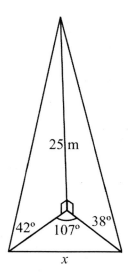

REVIEW SUMMARY

In this unit, you have learned how to . . .

- solve problems involving two right triangles in 2-D and in 3-D

- determine the value of angles from $0°$ to $180°$ by using the Sine and Cosine ratios

- determine two values for the sine of angles from $0°$ to $180°$

- apply the Sine Law to solve problems:

$$\frac{\sin A}{a} = \frac{\sin B}{b} = \frac{\sin C}{c} \quad \text{or} \quad \frac{a}{\sin A} = \frac{b}{\sin B} = \frac{c}{\sin C}$$

- apply the Cosine Law in either form as appropriate to solve problems:

$$a^2 = b^2 + c^2 - 2bc \cos A \qquad\qquad \cos A = \frac{b^2 + c^2 - a^2}{2bc}$$

PRACTICE TEST

1. Which of the following formulas works *only* with triangles that contain right angles?

    A. $\dfrac{\sin A}{a} = \dfrac{\sin B}{b}$

    B. $a^2 = b^2 + c^2 - 2bc \cos A$

    C. $\cos A = \dfrac{b^2 + c^2 - a^2}{2bc}$

    D. $\tan A = \dfrac{\text{opposite}}{\text{adjacent}}$

2. If $\sin \theta = \dfrac{3}{5}$, when $0 \le \theta \le 180°$, then the value of θ is

    A. $37°$

    B. $143°$

    C. $37°$ and $143°$

    D. $37°$ and $180°$

3. Find the indicated unknown side lengths or angles for each of the following triangles.

a)

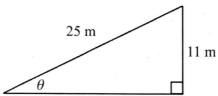

25 m

11 m

θ

b)

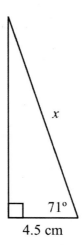

x

71°

4.5 cm

c)

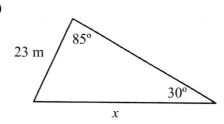

85°

23 m

30°

x

d)

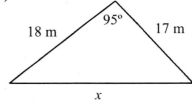

95°

18 m

17 m

x

e)

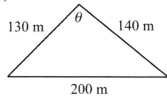

θ

130 m

140 m

200 m

f)

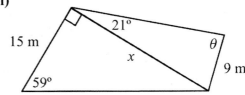

21°

15 m

x

θ

9 m

59°

4. A student wishes to measure the height of a tower. From a point several metres from the base of the tower, she measures the angle of elevation to be 58°. She moves 10 m directly away from the tower. She takes another measurement and finds the angle of elevation to be 49°. The angle measurements were taken at her eye level, which is 1.45 m from the ground. How high is the tower?

POLYNOMIALS

When you are finished this unit, you should be able to . . .

- solve problems involving arithmetic growth
- use expressions to represent general terms and sums for arithmetic growth and apply these expressions to solve problems
- factor a difference of squares, including cases that have a greatest common factor, $a^2x^2 - b^2y^2$
- factor single variable trinomials, including cases that require decomposition, $ax^2 + bx + c$
- find the product of polynomials
- divide polynomials by a binomial
- express the results of dividing polynomials by binomials with division statements

PREREQUISITE SKILLS AND KNOWLEDGE

Prior to beginning this unit, you should be able to . . .

- translate word problems into algebraic expressions
- factor basic polynomials using the inspection method
- determine the greatest common factors of terms
- complete long division questions
- determine and combine like terms in algebraic expressions

Lesson 1 ARITHMETIC SEQUENCES

NOTES

The three dots, . . ., indicate that the sequence continues on following the same pattern.

A number sequence is a list of numbers that are separated by commas. Some sequences follow rules or patterns. In particular, an arithmetic sequence is one in which each term is increasing or decreasing by the same set amount.

The following sequences are all arithmetic sequences:

2, 5, 8, 11, . . .

3 is added to each term to get the subsequent term.

4, 3.5, 3, 2.5, 2, . . .

−0.5 is added to each term to get the subsequent term.

$\dfrac{1}{4}, \dfrac{3}{8}, \dfrac{1}{2}, \dfrac{5}{8}, \ldots$

$\dfrac{1}{8}$ is added to each term to get the subsequent term.

The following sequences are **not** arithmetic sequences:

1, 3, 6, 10, 15, . . .

100, 50, 25, 12.5, . . .

They do each follow a pattern, but it is not the repeated addition of the same number, so the sequences are not arithmetic.

Example 1

Identify which of the following sequences are arithmetic.
For those that are arithmetic, state the number that is being added to each term.
a) 4, 9, 14, 19, . . .
b) 3, 6, 12, 24, . . .
c) 10, 4, −2, −8, . . .
d) $\dfrac{1}{3}, \dfrac{2}{3}, \dfrac{4}{3}, \dfrac{8}{3}, \ldots$
e) $\dfrac{4}{5}, \dfrac{6}{5}, \dfrac{8}{5}, 2, \ldots$

Solution

a) Arithmetic sequence. 5 is being added each time.
b) Not an arithmetic sequence.
c) Arithmetic sequence. −6 is added each time.
d) Not an arithmetic sequence.
e) Arithmetic sequence. $\dfrac{2}{5}$ is being added each time.

In order to generate a sequence, a starting value and the value that is being added are required. All terms can then be generated by repeatedly adding the same amount to each term.

Example 2

Generate five terms for the following arithmetic sequences:
a) Starting with 14, add 7 each time.
b) Starting with −3, add −10 each time.
c) Starting with 1.3, add −2.4 each time.
d) Starting with $\dfrac{1}{3}$, add $\dfrac{2}{3}$ each time.

Solution

a) 14, 21, 28, 35, 42
b) −3, −13, −23, −3, −43
c) 1.3, −1.1, −3.5, −5.9, −8.3
d) $\dfrac{1}{3}, 1, 1\dfrac{2}{3}, 2\dfrac{1}{3}, 3$

There are many real-life situations that exhibit arithmetic growth.

Example 3

Each year on his birthday, David's grandparents give him money.
They started on his first birthday by giving him $10.
Each birthday after that, they give him $5 more than they did the previous year.

a) Write a sequence that shows the amount that David receives on his first six birthdays.
b) How much will David receive on his 10th birthday?

Solution

a) 10, 15, 20, 25, 30, 35
b) 10, 15, 20, 25, 30, 35, 40, 45, 50, 55
    For his 10th birthday, David will receive $55.00

As the problems involving arithmetic sequences become more complex, it is useful to be able to work with them more formally, using formulas and specific variables for the various components of the sequence.

The following is a list of variables and what each one represents.

a: the first term in the sequence

d: the common difference. This number can be found by choosing any term in the sequence and subtracting the previous term.

n: the number of terms in the sequence. n is always a whole number.

t_n: the nth term in the sequence; also referred to as the general term

Example 4

In the following sequence, find a, d, n, and t_4.

2, 6, 10, 14, 18, 22

Solution
a: the first term is 2
d: the common difference is 4

$$10 - 6 = 4$$

$$or$$

$$14 - 10 = 4$$

n: there are 6 terms in the sequence

t_4: the 4th term in the sequence is 14

Sometimes, the characteristics of a sequence are known, but it is not convenient to write out the entire sequence in order to determine a particular term. This is when it is useful to have a formula that will generate the term.

This formula will generate any specified term for which a and d are known.

$$t_n = a + (n-1)d$$

It is called the general term formula.

Example 5

For the following arithmetic sequence, find the 20th term.

$4, 1, -2, -5, \ldots t_{20}$

The three dots indicate that the established pattern continues between the given values.

Solution

$a = 4$

$d = -3$

$n = 20$

Substitute into the formula:

$$t_n = a + (n-1)d$$
$$t_{20} = 4 + (20-1)(-3)$$
$$= 4 + (19)(-3)$$
$$= -53$$

The general term formula can be used to produce a linear function. This linear function can be used to generate any term in the sequence.

It should be noted that the general term formula produces discrete data and not continuous data as some linear functions do.

A linear function is a function that can be in the form $y = mx + b$.

Consider the arithmetic sequence in Example 5:

$4, 1, -2, -5, \ldots$

By substituting $a = 4$ and $d = -3$ into the general term formula, the general term of the sequence is produced.

$$t_n = a + (n-1)d$$
$$t_n = 4 + (n-1)(-3)$$
$$t_n = 4 + -3n + 3$$
$$t_n = -3n + 7$$

The general term that is produced is in the form of a linear function. This is true of the general term of all arithmetic sequences. They produce linear functions with graphs that are straight lines with a domain in the natural number set.

The table feature on the graphing calculator allows for a list of the entire sequence to be displayed.

Using the general term from above, $t_n = -3n + 7$, enter it into a graphing calculator in the form $y = -3x + 7$.

Produce a table of values:

x	y
1	4
2	1
3	–2
4	–5
5	–8
6	–11

Example 6

Given the arithmetic sequence
–5, 2, 9, 16, . . .
a) Find the general term.
b) Find t_{10} and t_{100}.
c) Determine which term is 79.
d) Enter the general term into your graphing calculator, and use it to create a table of values for the first ten terms of the sequence.

Solution
a) $a = -5$
$d = 7$
$t_n = a + (n-1)d$
$t_n = -5 + (n-1)(7)$
$t_n = 7n - 12$

b) $t_{10} = 7(10) - 12$
$t_{10} = 58$

$t_{100} = 7(100) - 12$
$t_{100} = 688$

c) $t_n = 7n - 12$

$79 = 7n - 12$

$91 = 7n$

$n = 13$

79 is the 13th term.

d) $t_n = 7n - 12$

$y = 7x - 12$

x	y
1	−5
2	2
3	9
4	16
5	23
6	30
7	37
8	44
9	51
10	58

Example 7

A particular arithmetic sequence has a common difference of −2.5 and $t_{41} = -64$. What is the first term in the sequence?

Solution

$t_n = -64$

$n = 41$

$d = -2.5$

$t_n = a + (n-1)d$

$-64 = a + (41-1)(-2.5)$

$-64 = a - 100$

$a = 36$

The first term is 36.

NOTES

Example 8

Amorita starts working for a company at a yearly salary of $19 000. Each year she gets a raise of $1 800.

a) How much will she be making during her fifth year with the company?
b) When will she make $40 600?
c) Will she ever make $150 000 per year or more? Explain your answer.

Solution
a) $a = 19\,000$

$d = 1\,800$

$t_n = a + (n-1)d$

$t_n = 19\,000 + (n-1)1\,800$

$t_n = 1\,800n + 17\,200$

5th year:
$t_5 = 1\,800(5) + 17\,200$

$t_5 = 26\,200$

She will make $26 200 in her 5th year.

b) $t_n = 40\,600$

$t_n = 1\,800n + 17\,200$

$40\,600 = 1\,800n + 17\,200$

$n = 13$

She will make $40 600 in her 13th year.

c) $150\,000 = 1\,800n + 12\,700$

$n = 73.7$

Since n must be a natural number, $n = 74$.

This means that she would have to work for 74 years to make more than $150 000. Since it is very unlikely that she would or could work that long, it is very unlikely that she will ever earn $150 000/year with this company.

If $n = 73.4$, the answer should still be 74 years as she needs 73 whole years and some of the 74th year to make more than $150 000.

PRACTICE EXERCISES

1. For each of the following arithmetic sequences, generate the next five terms.
    a) $15, -4, -23, \ldots$ -42

    b) $3.1, 5.7, 8.3, \ldots$

    c) $a = -3, d = 4$

2. Which of the following sequences is **not** an arithmetic sequence?
    A. $5, 10, 15, 20, \ldots$ B. $1, 2, 4, 8, 16, \ldots$

    C. $6, -2, -10, -18, \ldots$ D. $\frac{1}{2}, 1, 1\frac{1}{2}, 2, \ldots$

3. Give the general term and t_{30} for the following arithmetic sequences.
    a) $-10, -1, 8, \ldots$ b) $3.5, 2, 0.5, \ldots$

4. For a particular arithmetic sequence, $a = 25$ and $d = -15$.

    a) Find the general term.

    b) Which term is -245?

    c) Use a calculator table to display t_{10} to t_{15}.

5. Each summer, the price of an ice-cream cone increases by $0.15. In the 5th year, ice-cream cones cost $1.80.

    a) How much did ice-cream cones cost in the first year?

    b) How much will ice-cream cones cost in the 9th year?

    c) When will ice-cream cones cost $3.45?

Lesson 2 ARITHMETIC SERIES

When the commas in an arithmetic sequence are replaced with "+" signs, the sequence becomes a series.
Rewriting the sequence,
2, 5, 8, 11, 14

as a series gives us
2 + 5 + 8 + 11 + 14

One way of finding the sum of such a series is by adding all of the terms.

The sum of the series above is
2 + 5 + 8 + 11 + 14 = 40

When a series contains more terms, it is helpful to use formulas.

In the previous lesson, *a, d, n*, and t_n were defined and used in the general term formula.
These variables are also used when finding sums. The additional variable for sums is S_n.

S_n represents the sum of the first *n* terms in a series.

There are two formulas that can be used to find S_n:

$$S_n = \frac{n}{2}(a + t_n)$$

$$S_n = \frac{n}{2}\left[2a + (n-1)d\right]$$

The first formula is used when the first and last terms in the series are known, as well as the number of terms in the series.
The second formula is used when the first term, the common difference, and the number of terms in the series are all known.

Example 1

Find the sum of the following arithmetic series.

a) 1, . . . , 95   **b)** 41, 39, 37, . . .
    n = 21   *n* = 12

Solution

a) $a = 1$

$n = 21$

$t_n = 95$

$$S_n = \frac{n}{2}\left(a + \frac{t}{n}\right)$$

$$S_{21} = \frac{21}{2}(1 + 95)$$

$$S_{21} = 1\,008$$

b) $a = 41$

$n = 12$

$d = -2$

$$S_n = \frac{n}{2}\left[2a + (n-1)d\right]$$

$$S_{12} = \frac{12}{2}\left[2(41) + (12-1)(-2)\right]$$

$$S_{12} = 360$$

If two subsequent sums are known, such as S_{11} and S_{12}, their difference will be equal to the term with the same number as the second sum.

$$t_{12} = S_{12} - S_{11}$$

or, generally,

$$t_n = S_n - S_{(n-1)}$$

Example 2

In a particular arithmetic series, the sum of the first 10 terms is 110 and the sum of the first 11 terms is 132. What is the 11th term in the series?

Solution

$$t_n = S_n - S_{(n-1)}$$

$$t_{11} = S_{11} - S_{10}$$

$$t_{11} = 132 - 110$$

$$t_{11} = 22$$

There are many real-life problems that can be solved using the formulas for the sums of series.

Example 3

For eight weeks over the summer, Lexi had a job mowing lawns. She started by having 5 customers in her first week. Each week after that she had 2 more lawns to mow than she had during the previous week.

a) How many lawns did she mow in her 8th week?

b) How many lawns did she mow in total during the summer?

c) If she charged $6 per lawn, how much did she make during the first 6 weeks?

Solution

a) $a = 5$
    $d = 2$
    $n = 8$

Since we are interested in the number of lawns during the 8th week only, and not the total during all 8 weeks, we are just finding the 8th term so the general term formula should be used.

$$t_n = a + (n-1)d$$
$$t_n = 5 + (8-1)2$$
$$t_n = 19$$

She mowed 19 lawns in her 8th week.

b) Since the question now asks for the *total* number of lawns mowed over the 8 weeks, one of the S_n formulas will be used. Enough information is known to use either form of the sum formula.

$$S_n = \frac{n}{2}[a + t_n]$$
$$S_n = \frac{8}{2}[5 + 19]$$
$$S_n = 96$$

She mowed 96 lawns over the 8 weeks.

c) First, find the number of lawns mowed in the 6 weeks:

$a = 5$

$d = 2$

$n = 6$

$$S_n = \frac{n}{2}\left[2a + (n-1)d\right]$$

$$S_6 = \frac{6}{2}\left[2(5) + (6-1)2\right]$$

$$S_6 = 60$$

She mowed 60 lawns in the first 6 weeks.

Total earned $= 6(60) = 360$

She earned $360.00 mowing lawns in the first 6 weeks.

PRACTICE EXERCISES

1. Which of the following series is an arithmetic series?
   A. $5 + 10 + 20 + 40$
   B. $5 + 10 + 15 + 20$
   C. $5, 10, 20, 40$
   D. $5, 10, 15, 20$

2. For each of the following arithmetic series, find the indicated sum.
   a) $14 + 21 + 28, \ldots$

   $$S_{10}$$

   b) $10 + \ldots -144$

   $$S_8$$

   c) $\dfrac{2}{5} + \dfrac{4}{5} + \dfrac{6}{5} \ldots$

   $$S_{11}$$

3. The day after Halloween, a child counts the number of treats that he has and finds that he has 71 treats. He tells his mother that he will eat 2 treats on the first day, and each day after that, he will eat 3 more treats than the day before. His mother says that he can do that if he throws away everything that he has left after 6 days.

a) How many treats will the child eat during the 6 days?

b) How many will be thrown out after the 6th day?

4. The sum of the first 8 terms of a particular arithmetic series is 14.
The sum of the first 9 terms of the same series is 27. What is the 9th term of the series?

Lesson 3   POLYNOMIALS

To begin the investigation into polynomials, consider the following phrases and ideas.

Variable

A variable is a letter, often x or y or a, etc., that represents a number. Sometimes by solving an equation, it is found that a variable represents more than one number. An example of this is the equation $x^2 = 4$, which has the two solutions of $x = 2$ and $x = -2$. Some variables used in mathematics are letters borrowed from the Greek alphabet, such as θ (theta), which is commonly used to represent a trigonometric degree.

Variable Degree

Each variable has an exponent, sometimes referred to as the power of that variable. The value of that exponent is equal to the degree of the variable. In this unit, the degrees will all be positive integers (including zero).

Degree 1: An example of a variable of degree 1 is x. This could be written as x^1, but as is common in mathematics, an understood value of 1 is not usually written.

Degree 2: An example of a variable of degree 2 is x^2. This is "x raised to the exponent two" or "x squared."

Degree 0: The degree zero case is a special one. Whenever any variable has an exponent of zero, the result is the value 1; $x^0 = 1$. The degree-zero variable produces a constant, and as such, any constant can be considered to be multiplied by a degree-zero variable.

Terms

A variable and all that it is multiplied by forms a single term. The variable may be multiplied by other variables, or a number, or both. Examples of terms include x, $2x$, $3xy$, $4x^2$, $5x^2y$, and 6. Note that the last term given, 6, does not show a variable but it is still a term. Terms that do not include variables are referred to as constant terms. The numbers in the other terms given are attached to variables of degrees greater than zero. These numbers are not called constants, but rather coefficients or numerical coefficients.

Monomial

A single term is called a monomial. Monomials can be strung together by addition or subtraction to form a series of monomials. When this occurs, the series takes on a new name derived from the number of individual terms involved. One general name for the series of monomials, regardless of their number, is polynomial.

$3x$ = monomial

$x + 5y^2$ = binomial

$-4x + 2y + 5$ = trinomial

Polynomial

The smallest series of monomials is the individual monomial, which is only one term. When two monomials (two terms) are added or subtracted, the polynomial is called a **binomial**. When three monomials are added or subtracted, the polynomial is called a **trinomial**. The prefixes mono-, bi-, and tri- are adopted from the Greek language. Prefixes do exist for numbers greater than three. However, for any polynomial with more than three terms, the term **polynomial** is used.

Monomial Degree

The degree of any monomial is found by adding all the exponents from each variable in that term. Constants are degree zero, so do not add them to the monomial degree. E.g., $5x^2y$ has a degree of 3.

Polynomial Degree

The degree of a polynomial is **not** found by adding the degrees of each of the monomial terms. Rather, the degree of a polynomial is equal to the degree of the highest degree monomial (above). If the polynomial in question is a monomial, then the polynomial has the same degree as that monomial. E.g., $3x^5y^2 + 2x^4 + 3y$ has a degree of 7.

Example 1

Two polynomials are given below. Indicate how many terms each polynomial consists of and name that polynomial. For each term, indicate the variables that are used and the degree of each variable. State the overall degree of each term, the degree of the polynomial, and indicate any constants present.

$$2x^2 - 3xy - z \qquad\qquad -8x^3 + 2$$

Solution

There are three terms in the polynomial $2x^2 - 3xy - z$, which makes it a trinomial. The first term has one variable, x, and it is of degree 2. The second term has x and y, each of degree 1. The overall degree of the second term is 2. The third term is z, a variable of degree 1. The overall degree of the polynomial is equal to the greatest degree, which in this case is 2. There are no constants present, only numerical coefficients.

There are two terms in the polynomial $-8x^3 + 2$, which makes it a binomial. The first term has only one variable, x, and it is of degree 3. The second term has no visible variable (degree zero), so this is a constant term. The second term is considered to have a degree of zero. The overall degree of this polynomial is 3 and the 2 is the constant.

Like Terms

Variables are used to represent numbers whose values are not known until an equation is solved or additional information is given. An expression such as $x + y$ cannot be made simpler. However, $x + x$ can be simplified without knowing the value of the variable, such as $x + x = 2x$. Constants can be added as can normal numbers: $3 + 4 = 7$. It is not possible to add $x + x^2$ without further information. In the cases above, the terms can only be added when they contain the same variable(s) of the same degree.

Note that constants (numbers) are considered to have any variable of degree zero.

Example 2

Simplify these **like** terms: $x + x$, $2xy - xy$, $-3x^2y + 5x^2y$, $3 + 2$.

Solution

Adding or subtracting these binomials with like terms gives $2x$, xy, $2x^2y$, and 5, respectively.

When the binomials above were simplified, they produced monomials. Any number of like terms can be combined into a single term.

Unlike Terms

If one term has a variable that is different from another term, or if the first term has a variable of a different degree from the same variable of another term, then they are **unlike** terms. It is important to stress that two terms can be unlike even if they have the same variable (just of a different degree). Also, note that the numerical coefficients do not determine whether terms are like or unlike.

Example 3

Rearrange the terms on the right-hand side so they line up with their like terms on the left-hand side.

$2x$	-3
$-4y^3z$	$-6y^3$
23	x^2y
$2x^2y$	y^3z
$2x^2y^2$	$-2x$
y^3	$9x^2y^2$

Solution

$2x$	$-2x$
$-4y^3z$	y^3z
23	-3
$2x^2y$	x^2y
$2x^2y^2$	$9x^2y^2$
y^3	$-6y^3$

ADDITION AND SUBTRACTION OF POLYNOMIALS

The ability to combine like terms is the key to the addition and subtraction of polynomials. Consider the following examples.

Example 4

Simplify the expression by combining like terms.

$2x + x^2 - 1 + 3x + x^2 + 1$

Solution

$2x + x^2 - 1 + 3x + x^2 + 1$

$(x^2 + x^2) + (2x + 3x) - 1 + 1$

$2x^2 + 5x$

In example 4, a polynomial consisting of a number of terms was simplified to a binomial by combining like terms. A polynomial should always be simplified fully, especially if it is being named based on the number of terms present.

Example 5

Add the following polynomials.

$(3x + y + xy) + (2x + 3y - 2xy + y^2)$

Solution

First of all, note the brackets. In this case, the brackets simply identify where the two polynomials are located in this list of terms being added. This is a trinomial plus a polynomial. Clearing the brackets in this case is simply a matter of removing them from the expression. There are cases where the brackets must be dealt with first, before combining like terms (see next example). Second, note that there is a term, y^2, that has no like terms to combine with. This does not interfere with combining the available like terms.

$5x + 4y - xy + y^2$

The two polynomials are added to produce a single polynomial.

Example 6

Add the following trinomials. Express the answer by listing the degree terms in descending order.

$2(x^2 - 2x - 1) + (3x^2 + 5x + 7)$

Solution

Clear the brackets first, then group like terms.

$2(x^2 - 2x - 1) + (3x^2 + 5x + 7)$

$2x^2 - 4x - 2 + (3x^2 + 5x + 7)$

$5x^2 + x + 5$

Note that the polynomials were listed with the highest degree terms first, so no rearrangement was necessary.

Use the distributive property to multiply the number 2 outside of the brackets with each term inside the brackets.

ORDER OF POWERS AND LEADING COEFFICIENTS

In example 6 above, the answer was required to be written in descending order. That is, the term with the highest exponent value goes first, and then the remaining terms go in decreasing order until the constant is the final term. This is generally done only with single variable polynomials. If there are multiple variables, the degree of each term must be determined by adding the exponents of each variable in the term. If there is only one variable, the degree is simply the value of the exponent.
The highest degree term becomes the degree of the polynomial.

When a polynomial is written in descending order, the numerical coefficient for the term with the highest exponent is named the leading coefficient. In the example above, the leading coefficient is 5.

PRACTICE EXERCISES

1. How many different variables are present in the polynomial $x^2 + 2xy + z + 4$?

   A. 2
   B. 3
   C. 4
   D. 5

2. What is the degree of each term in the polynomial $2x^2y + xyz - 3y$? What is the overall degree of the polynomial?

$2xy = 3$

$xyz = 3$

3

$-3y = 1$

3. A binomial with no like terms is added to a trinomial with no like terms (and there are no like terms between the two polynomials). How many terms will there be in the resulting polynomial?

5

4. Combine like terms and simplify the polynomial $2x^2 + 3y^3 - x - y^3 + 4x - 2y^3 + 11$. What is the degree of the resulting polynomial?

$2x^2 + 3x + y \ 11$

$degree = 2$

5. Add and subtract the following polynomials by clearing the brackets first and then simplifying by combining like terms.

$$2(x+1)+3(x^2-2)-(x-1)$$

$2x+2+3x^2-6-x+1$

$x-3+3x^2$

6. Simplify the following expression. Write the resulting polynomial with its degree terms in descending order.

$$3(1-x)+2(2-x^2)-3(4-x)$$

$3-3x+4-2x^2-12+3x$

$2x^2-5$

Lesson 4 *MULTIPLICATION OF POLYNOMIALS*

In order to multiply polynomials, the distributive property and the laws of exponents need to be used. In this lesson, examples of the distributive property will be provided starting with the simplest examples and working up to the distribution (multiplication) of multiple polynomials.

The following examples illustrate a basic aspect of the distributive property:

$$5(3) = 4(3) + 1(3) \qquad 5(3) = 3(3) + 2(3) \qquad 5(3) = 2(3) + 3(3)$$
$$15 = 12 + 3 \qquad\qquad 5(3) = 9 + 6 \qquad\qquad 15 = 6 + 9$$
$$15 = 15 \qquad\qquad\quad 15 = 15 \qquad\qquad\quad 15 = 15$$

Look at the examples above and notice that the right-hand side equals the left-hand side. This basic aspect of the distributive property can be expressed in a general equation as

$$a(x) + b(x) = (a + b)(x)$$

The directing word "expand" may be used when it is necessary to multiply polynomials and simplify.

Note that in Lesson 1, a few questions involved the clearing of brackets. This represents the distributive property as well.

$$2(x^2 + 2x - 3)$$
$$2x^2 + 4x - 6$$

The factor of 2 was distributed throughout the trinomial above by multiplying each term by 2. Now consider the same polynomial above, multiplied by a larger factor.

$$5(x^2 + 2x - 3)$$

The new factor to distribute is 5. Consider the following example.

Example 1

First, clear the brackets for $5(x^2 + 2x - 3)$ as usual. Now, using the distributive property illustrated above, break the factor 5 down into $(3 + 2)$ and then multiply. Compare the answers.

Solution

$$5(x^2 + 2x - 3) \qquad\qquad (3 + 2)(x^2 + 2x - 3)$$
$$5x^2 + 10x - 15 \qquad\qquad 3(x^2 + 2x - 3) + 2(x^2 + 2x - 3)$$
$$\qquad\qquad\qquad\qquad\quad 3x^2 + 6x - 9 + 2x^2 + 4x - 6$$
$$5x^2 + 10x - 15 \qquad\qquad 5x^2 + 10x - 15$$

The answers are identical. The steps involved in the second method involved combining like terms.

LAW OF EXPONENTS

At this point in the examination of the distributive property, it is necessary to review the law of exponents.

$$x^a \cdot x^b = x^{a+b}$$

Exponents are added when two identical variables are multiplied.

$$x^3(x^5) = x^8$$

In Lesson 1, like and unlike terms were investigated, and it was found that unlike terms could not be added or subtracted. When multiplying, the law of exponents allows the exponents of identical variables to be added.

Example 2

Multiply the two monomials below, and simplify by multiplying the coeffiecients and applying the law of exponents when applicable.

$$2x^2y \qquad\qquad -3xy^3z$$

Solution

$$(2x^2y)(-3xy^3z)$$
$$-6x^3y^4z$$

The two coefficients were multiplied. The variable x was present in each term, so after multiplication, it is written only once with its exponents added. This is also the case with the variable y. The variable z remained unchanged.

MULTIPLICATION (MONOMIAL TIMES BINOMIAL) AND (MONOMIAL TIMES TRINOMIAL)

Example 3

Distribute the monomial into the given binomial and trinomial.

$$(2xy)(3x^2 - 1) \qquad\qquad (2xy)(3x^2 + x - 1)$$

Solution

$$(2xy)(3x^2 - 1) \qquad\qquad (2xy)(3x^2 + x - 1)$$
$$6x^3y - 2xy \qquad\qquad 6x^3y + 2x^2y - 2xy$$

NOTES

Note that a monomial multiplied by a binomial produces two terms, just as $1 \times 2 = 2$.

The monomial multiplied by a trinomial produces three terms, just as $1 \times 3 = 3$. If there are like terms, simplification occurs at the end.

MULTIPLICATION OF TWO BINOMIALS

Consider the distributive property when multiplying the following binomials.

$(x+1)(x+2)$

Break this down into $x(x+2) + 1(x+2)$, clear the brackets by distributing, then combine like terms.

$x^2 + 2x + 1x + 2$

$x^2 + 3x + 2$

The process of multiplying two binomials is sometimes introduced to students using the acronym FOIL as a means of memorizing the process. Unfortunately, memorizing terms associated with the letters of FOIL sometimes replaces the understanding of the distributive property.

Note that the binomial multiplied by a binomial produced four terms.
$(2 \cdot 2 = 4)$. However, since there were like terms, simplification resulted in the given trinomial.

MULTIPLYING A BINOMIAL AND A TRINOMIAL

By continuing to employ the distributive property, we see that the multiplication of a binomial times a trinomial should produce six individual terms before any simplification. The methods should become quite familiar.

Example 4

A rectangular box has a volume determined by multiplying its base area by its height. The base area is given by the formula $x^2 + x + 1$. The height is given as $x + 2$. Find the volume of the box as a general polynomial, and then as an exact value if $x = 2$ cm.

The volume formula for a rectangular prism can be written as $V = Bh$, where B is the area of the base $(l \times w)$, or as $V = lwh$.

Solution

$V = Bh$

$V = (x+2)(x^2 + x + 1)$

$V = x(x^2 + x + 1) + 2(x^2 + x + 1)$

$V = x^3 + x^2 + x + 2x^2 + 2x + 2$

$V = x^3 + 3x^2 + 3x + 2$

This polynomial, before simplification, had the expected six terms $2 \times 3 = 6$. To find the exact volume, place the given value into the equation for the variable.

$$V = (2)^3 + 3(2)^2 + 3(2) + 2$$
$$V = 8 + 12 + 6 + 2$$
$$V = 28$$

The box has a volume of 28 cm^3.

MULTIPLICATION OF THREE BINOMIALS

When the required multiplication involves more than two polynomials, the problem is solved in multiple steps.
First, multiply any two of the polynomials (in this case any two of the binomials). Then, simplify if possible. Finally, multiply this answer by the final polynomial.

The initial multiplication of two binomials will produce four terms. If there are like terms, this will simplify to a trinomial (or less). This answer can then be distributed through the final binomial.

Example 5

A three-dimensional solid has sides defined by the following binomials: $(x+1), (y+1)$, and $(z+1)$. Determine a general polynomial that defines the volume of this solid.

Solution
Volume is determined by multiplying the three dimensions (sides).

$$(x+1)(y+1)(z+1)$$
$$[x(y+1) + 1(y+1)](z+1)$$
$$[xy + x + y + 1](z+1)$$
$$xy(z+1) + x(z+1) + y(z+1) + 1(z+1)$$
$$xyz + xy + xz + x + yz + y + z + 1$$

Since there are no like terms, the resulting polynomial has eight terms $2 \times 2 \times 2 = 8$.

First, multiply any two binomials and simplify if possible.

Second, multiply the answer from the first step by the remaining binomial.

PRACTICE EXERCISES

1. Distribute and simplify the expression $2(x+1)(x+3)-3(2x)$.

$$2x+2+x+3-6x$$

$$3x-6x+5+x$$

$$-2x+5$$

2. When $(x+1)$ is multiplied by $(x-1)$, the result is
   A. 1
   B. a monomial
   C. a binomial
   D. a trinomial

3. Evaluate the expressions $(x+a)^2$ and $(x+b)^2$. What observations can be made regarding the constants a and b and the numerical coefficients of the second term in the expanded polynomials?

$$(x+a)(x+a)$$

$$x^2+xa+xa+a^2$$

$$x^2+2xa+a^2$$

4. Expand and simplify the expression $(x+1)(x+2)(x+3)$.

$$x^2+2x+x+2$$

$$x^2+3x+2$$

$$x^2(x+3)+3x(x+3)+2(x+3)$$

$$x^3+3x^2+3x^2+9x+2x+6$$

$$x^3+6x^2+11x+6$$

5. Each side of a cubic box is defined as $(x+1)$. A smaller cubic box, with each side equal to x, is placed inside the larger box. What volume of free space is still available in the larger box if $x = 1$ cm? Provide the polynomial that represents the volume of each box.

$$12(x+1)$$

$$12x+12$$

6. If $(x^4 + 2x^2)$ is multiplied by $(x^3 + x - 1)$, the degree of the resulting polynomial is

   A. 7
   B. 8
   C. 9
   D. unknown

$$x^3(x^4+2x^2) + x(x^4+2x^2) - 1(x^4+2x^2)$$

$$x^7 + 2x^5 + x^5 + 2x^3 - x^4 - 2x^2$$

$$x^7 - x^4 + x^5 + 2x^5 + 2x^3 - 2x^2$$

$$x^8 + 2x^5 + 2x^3 - 2x^2$$

Lesson 5 FACTORING POLYNOMIALS

NOTES

To begin an investigation into the factoring of polynomials, it is useful to review a number of related topics.

Factoring Numbers

Any number can always be expressed as a product of two numbers. If the number is a prime number, the product is simply the number 1 and the original number. Most numbers can be expressed using multiple product pairs. Consider the number 20.

$$20 = (2)(10)$$
$$20 = (4)(5)$$
$$20 = (20)(1)$$

The number is broken down into factors. Each of the numbers on the right-hand side of the equation is a factor of 20. As well as considering the positive set of numbers, it is necessary to consider that two negative numbers produce a positive product.

$$20 = (-2)(-10)$$
$$20 = (-4)(-5)$$
$$20 = (-20)(-1)$$

Multiplying Binomials

In the previous lesson, the skills necessary to multiply (and simplify) binomials were examined.

$(x+1)(x+4) = x^2 + 5x + 4$ (not all distribution and simplification steps are shown)

This multiplication also reveals that $(x+1)$ and $(x+4)$ are factors of $x^2 + 5x + 4$ because there is no remainder. In this lesson, the skills necessary to reverse the multiplication process will be examined.

Multiplying a Polynomial by a Constant

One of the basic skills learned for simplifying polynomials involved adding and subtracting polynomials. Before this can be accomplished, any brackets must be cleared by distribution.

$$3(x^2 + 3x - 5)$$
$$3x^2 + 9x - 15$$

FACTORING OUT A GREATEST COMMON FACTOR (GCF)

Whenever a question or problem involves a polynomial greater than a monomial, it is useful to observe whether or not each term has a common factor greater than 1.

Example 1

Find any common factors between each term of the trinomial $2x^2 + 4x + 8$.

Solution

Every term has a factor of 2 that can be removed. In other words, each term can be divided by 2. No other factors are common to each term.

Remove a 2 from each term, and rewrite as follows:

$$2(x^2 + 2x + 4)$$

At this point, it is useful to once again look at the new trinomial for more common factors. Since there are no more, the next step is to factor the polynomial.

Example 2

What is the GCF (greatest common factor) for
$24x^2y + 16xy - 32x$?

Solution

In this instance, the trinomial has more than just a constant in common between the factors. Each term contains the variable x as well. A common factor of 2 could be removed from each term, but this is not the greatest constant that they all have in common. In fact, a factor of 8 could be removed from each term. Whether the 8 and the x are removed in one or more steps, the end result will be the same.

$$8x(3xy + 2y - 4)$$

At this point, the polynomial is simplified. The resulting polynomial (in brackets) cannot be factored further. Only certain types of polynomials will be factored at this level of mathematics.

FACTORING TRINOMIALS WITH A LEADING COEFFICIENT OF ONE

A polynomial may appear initially in the form $ax^2 + bx + c,$ where the leading coefficient is $a = 1$. This form of polynomial may also appear when a greatest common factor is removed from each term of a trinomial.

$3x^2 + 6x - 9$

$3(x^2 + 2x - 3)$

This type of factoring may be referred to as the inspection method.

In the simplification above, the trinomial can be factored. When all factors are listed for the **original** trinomial, the 3 must be listed as a factor as well.

Consider the following binomial products, noting the relationship between the constants in each binomial, and the resulting coefficients and constants in the trinomial formed.

$(x+1)(x+2)$ $\qquad$ $(x+2)(x+3)$

$x(x+2)+1(x+2)$ $\qquad$ $x(x+3)+2(x+3)$

$x^2 + 2x + 1x + 2$ $\qquad$ $x^2 + 3x + 2x + 6$

$x^2 + 3x + 2$ $\qquad$ $x^2 + 5x + 6$

$\qquad (x+3)(x+4)$

$\qquad x(x+4)+3(x+4)$

$\qquad x^2 + 4x + 3x + 12$

$\qquad x^2 + 7x + 12$

Each binomial had a leading coefficient of 1, and the resulting leading coefficient for the trinomial is also 1.

The distributive property results in a numerical coefficient for the x term, which is equal to the two initial binomial constants **added together**.

The final constant of the resulting trinomial is equal to the **product** of the original constants.

Example 3

Solve the following problem using the information stated above. Then, solve by distributing and simplification. Compare your answers.

$(x+3)(x-2)$

Solution

According to the information given, it can be expected that

- the leading coefficients for the binomials are each 1, so the leading coefficient for the resulting trinomial will also be 1

- the constants from the initial binomials should add together to produce the numerical coefficient for the x term in the trinomial. Here, there is a negative constant, so the sum is $+3+(-2)=1$.

- the constants should multiply together and produce the trinomial constant, which is $(+3)(-2)=-6$

The resulting trinomial, given all the above expectations, is x^2+x-6. Now, solve by distribution and simplification.

$(x+3)(x-2)$
$x(x-2)+3(x-2)$
$x^2-2x+3x-6$
x^2+x-6

The results are the same.

Example 4

Factor the trinomial $x^2-4x-21$ into two binomials.

Solution

The leading coefficient is 1, and there are no common factors to remove.
The binomials will take the form of $(x+a)(x+b)$, where the following is known:

$a+b=-4$
$(a)(b)=-21$

Recall that factoring means to write the polynomials as a product of factors.

To determine the factors, you can use the following set up:

Product | Numbers

Sum

For example,

$$P=-21\begin{array}{|c}3\\\hline-7\end{array}$$

$$S=-4$$

To solve this, consider what two numbers will produce -21 as a product and -4 as a sum. The only possibilities are $(1)(-21), (-1)(21), (3)(-7),$ and $(-3)(7)$. The only pair that adds up to -4 is $(3)(-7)$. This helps us to fully factor the trinomial.

The trinomial becomes

$x^2 + 3x - 7x - 21$

$\left(x^2 + 3x\right) + \left(-7x - 21\right)$

Factor:

$x(x+3) - 7(x+3)$

$(x+3)(x-7)$

So, the factors as two binomials are $(x+3)$ and $(x-7)$.

Example 5

List all the factors for the polynomials $2x^2 - 10x + 12$.

Solution

First, remove the GCF:

$2(x^2 - 5x + 6)$

Remember that the factored out constant will be a factor to list in the final answer.

Now, factor the trinomial:

$(x+a)(x+b)$

$a + b = -5$

$(a)(b) = +6$

Recall that two negative numbers multiply to give a positive number, and since the two constants add to a negative total, both must be negative. The answer will be two negative numbers that add to -5 and multiply to $+6$.

$(x-3)(x-2)$

All the factors for $2x^2 - 10x + 12$ are $(2)(x-3)(x-2)$.

PRACTICE EXERCISES

1. The GCF for the terms $23x^2yz$, $3xyz$, $6xy$, and $9x$ is

   A. 1
   B. $3x$
   C. $9x$
   D. x

2. List all the possible combinations of two numbers that, when multiplied together, equal -12.

   $-6, 2$ $\qquad$ $-3, 4$
   $-1, 12$ $\qquad$ $-4, 3$
   $12, -1$
   $2, -6$

3. What is the resulting polynomial when $4 - 3x - x^2$ is multiplied by a factor of -1?

   $-4 + 3x + x^2$

4. What is the value of the unknown variable, a, in the expression $(x+a)(x-5) = x^2 + 5x - 50$?

   $x^2 - 5x + ax - 5a$ $\qquad\qquad$ $a = 10$

5. Factor the expression $6x + 3x^2 + 5 - 2x - x^2 - 3$.

6. a) Find a pair of binomials that produces the trinomial $x^2 - 6x + a$ for any value of a. What value of a results?

b) Now, try this challenging question that requires an extension of what you've learned. What is a value of a that can never be produced?

PRACTICE QUIZ

1. How many terms does a trinomial have?

    A. 0

    B. 1

    C. 2

    D. 3

2. What is another name for a binomial?

3. An example of a polynomial that has a term of degree 3 is

    A. $3x^2 + 3x + 3$

    B. $2x^2y + y^2$

    C. $2x + 3y + 4z$

    D. $3xy + 11$

4. State the constant, the leading coefficient, and the number of numerical coefficients (not counting the leading coefficient or constant) in the polynomial $-2a^2 - bab + 3c - 5d + 11$.

5. Create a like term for each of the following two terms. The new like term cannot be identical to the given term.

    $7xyz$ and $16y^3$

6. What is the result of $(3xy^3)(-2x^3yz)$?

    $-2x_{yz}^3(3xy^3)$

    $-6x^4y^4z$

7. A student multiplies a trinomial by a binomial and then by another binomial. Before any simplification, how many terms should the student expect to see in the answer?

8. After removing a GCF of $-2x$ from a polynomial, the binomial $2x - x^2$ is formed. Write the equation of the original polynomial with the terms in descending order.

9. If $(x+1)(x-a) = x^2 - x - 2$, what is the value of a?

   A. -2
   B. -1
   C. 1
   D. 2

10. Distribute and simplify the expression $(4x)(x-3)(x-3)$.

Lesson 6   FACTORING A DIFFERENCE OF SQUARES

An important set of polynomials comprises those polynomials in the form $x^2 - c^2$. That is, a binomial with a leading coefficient of 1 attached to a squared variable. The second term is a constant squared, and this is subtracted from the first term.

Example 1

Is $x^2 - 64$ a difference of squares?

Solution

This can be written as $x^2 - 8^2$ and so yes, it is a difference of squares, where $c = 8$.

Why is this set of polynomials important, and how can they be factored? The answers to these two questions are related. This type of polynomial set is important because of the frequency of its appearance in mathematics and its simplicity. To factor polynomials of this type, consider the following examples:

$(x+1)(x-1)$ $\qquad$ $(x+2)(x-2)$ $\qquad$ $(x+c)(x-c)$

$x(x-1)+1(x-1)$ $\qquad$ $x(x-2)+2(x-2)$ $\qquad$ $x(x-c)+c(x-c)$

$x^2-x+x-1$ $\qquad$ $x^2-2x+2x-4$ $\qquad$ $x^2-cx+cx-c^2$

x^2-1 $\qquad$ x^2-4 $\qquad$ x^2-c^2

Notice the pattern of the binomials that create the difference of squares. Each initial binomial is identical except for the fact that one constant is being added, and the second constant is being subtracted. The constant in the final difference of squares is just the initial constant (from either binomial) squared. This constant is subtracted from the squared variable.

It is important that the constant in each initial binomial be the same absolute value (the same number, but one is negative and one is positive).

Example 2

Does the multiplication $(x+3)(x-4)$ create a difference of squares?

Solution

$(x+3)(x-4)$

$x(x-4)+3(x-4)$

$x^2-4x+3x-12$

x^2-x-12

No, the result is a trinomial, not a difference of squares. The initial binomials did not have the same constant being added and subtracted.

DIFFERENCE OF SQUARES ($a^2x^2 - c^2$)

As stated earlier, the simplicity of this type of polynomial emphasizes its importance. Up to this point, the investigation into polynomials and their factors has involved a leading coefficient of 1. Occasionally, every term had a coefficient other than 1, but after a GCF was removed the leading coefficient of 1 would emerge.

The leading coefficient need not be 1 if it can be expressed as a number squared.

Example 3

Simplify $(2x+1)(2x-1)$.

Solution
$2x(2x-1)+1(2x-1)$
$4x^2-2x+2x-1$
$4x^2-1$

A difference of squares is produced by the product of these two binomials. The binomials are identical with the exception that one adds its constant, and the other subtracts it. The final resulting difference of squares (DOS) can be surmised from either of the original binomials.

Original binomial: $(2x+1)$ or $(2x-1)$

Resulting DOS: $4x^2-1$

The first term in the DOS is equal to the first term from either binomial squared. The constant in the DOS is equal to either binomial constant squared. The constant is subtracted.

Example 4

Predict the resulting difference of squares that would result from the multiplication of $(3x+a)(3x-a)$.

Solution

The square of the first term of the binomial is $9x^2$. The square of the constant term of either binomial is a^2. This will be subtracted. The final difference of squares will be the binomial $9x^2-a^2$.

This result can be confirmed through distribution and simplification.

DIFFERENCE OF SQUARES ($a^2x^2 - b^2y^2$)

In this form of DOS, the constant term has been replaced with a variable that has a numerical coefficient. However, since the terms are all squared, and the second term is subtracted, this is still a difference of squares.

Example 5

Simplify $(3x + 5y)(3x - 5y)$.

Solution

$3x(3x - 5y) + 5y(3x - 5y)$

$9x^2 - 15xy + 15xy - 25y^2$

$9x^2 - 25y^2$

The first term in the DOS is the first binomial term squared. The second term in the DOS is the second term of either binomial squared. The second term is subtracted from the first term.

The order of the binomials is not relevant as $(x + 1)(x - 1)$ is equal to $(x - 1)(x + 1)$.

Example 6

Find the initial binomials that would produce the difference of squares binomial $16x^2 - 25y^2$.

Solution

Working backward determines what term, when squared, would give $16x^2$. The desired term is $4x$. Similarily, the term when squared that produces $25y^2$ is $5y$. So, the binomials are $(4x + 5y)$ and $(4x - 5y)$.

Difference of square binomials, like other polynomials, do not always appear in their simplest form. Sometimes, a common factor must be removed before the factoring process can continue.

Example 7

Factor $12x^3 - 243x$.

Solution

$3x(4x^2 - 81)$

$3x(2x + 9)(2x - 9)$

HIGHER EXPONENT DIFFERENCE OF SQUARES

In this investigation of the factoring of the difference of squares polynomials, the examples and problems have gradually increased in difficulty.

The simplest form, such as $x^2 - 1$, factors into $(x+1)(x-1)$.

Next, if the leading coefficient is greater than 1, such as $4x^2 - 1$, this factors into $(2x+1)(2x-1)$.

Consider the case where the binomial is $x^4 - 1$. This can be expressed as a difference of squares as well, with the factors being $(x^2 + 1)(x^2 - 1)$. Note also that now the second binomial is itself a difference of squares, so the factoring continues to $(x^2 + 1)(x+1)(x-1)$.

PRACTICE EXERCISES

1. Factor the difference of squares binomial $x^2 - 36$.

2. Completely factor $4x^4 - 36x^2$.

3. Completely factor $x^8 - 16$.

4. A farmer has 20 m of fencing and wants to enclose a rectangular plot of land. The farmer could create a square with each side measuring 5 m, which would result in a plot with a perimeter of 20 m and all the fencing being used up. However, the farmer decides to increase the length of two parallel sides, each by x metres. Therefore, each width will also decrease by the same x metres.

    a) How will the new area be calculated? (Show the simplified formula.)

    b) Calculate the area for the plot of land with sides that are 5 m each.
    Then, calculate the area that results when each of the two parallel sides is increased by 1 m, 2 m, and then 3 m.

5. The expression $9x^2 - 49$ is a difference of squares in which one factor is $(ax + b)$.
   What would the product of $(a)(b)$ be?

   A. 9
   B. 21
   C. 441
   D. $ax - b$

6. Factor $(x+1)^2 - 9$ as a difference of squares. Then, substitute the value $x = 2$ into both the original equation and the factored form and see if the answers are equal.
   Try any other value as well.

Lesson 7 FACTORING USING DECOMPOSITION OF POLYNOMIALS

This lesson investigates methods used to factor polynomials of the form $ax^2 + bx + c$, where the leading coefficient (a) is not 1, nor does it become 1 by factoring out a greatest common factor.

Consider a product of two binomials, where at least one has a leading coefficient that is not 1 and will not revert to 1 after removing a GCF.

$(2x+3)(x+5)$

$2x(x+5)+3(x+5)$

$2x^2+10x+3x+15$

$2x^2+13x+15$

The method, known as decomposition, allows a polynomial of this type to be factored as follows:

Given $2x^2+13x+15$, compare this to the general form ax^2+bx+c.

Here $a=2$, $b=13$, and $c=15$.

Multiply $(a)(c)$ to obtain a product that will be used to decompose b.

Here, $(a)(c)=(2)(15)=30$.

Now, find any two factors of 30 that when added, equal b, or 13. Recall that negative numbers may be factors.

Two factors that work in this instance are 3 and 10, as $3+10=13$ and $(3)(10)=30$.

Now, break up (decompose) the middle term into two like terms, using the two factors just found.

$2x^2+13x+15$ or $2x^2+13x+15$

$2x^2+10x+3x+15$ $2x^2+3x+10x+15$

The order that the decomposition is written in does not matter (both decompositions above work).

Find common factors between the first two terms and the last two terms, and factor them out. This is called grouping.

$2x(x+5)+3(x+5)$ or $x(2x+3)+5(2x+3)$

By the distributive property, this can be rewritten as its equivalent:

$(2x+3)(x+5)$ or $(x+5)(2x+3)$

Not only are both sides equal, they are the complete factoring of the trinomial.

NOTES

Note that the same steps for the inspection method can also be used with decomposition:

$$P = ac \quad \bigg|\; 3$$
$$= 30 \quad \bigg|\; 10$$

$$\text{sum} = 10$$
$$= 13$$

Example 1

Use the distributive property to expand the following and simplify. Then, work back using the decomposition method (showing all steps) to restore the original.

$(3x - 5)(2x + 3)$

Solution

$(3x - 5)(2x + 3)$

$3x(2x + 3) - 5(2x + 3)$

$6x^2 + 9x - 10x - 15$

$6x^2 - x - 15$

Now, compare with $ax^2 + bx + c$:

$(a)(c) = (6)(-15) = -90$

What factors of -90 will also add to give b, or -1?

The factors are $-10, +9$.

$6x^2 - 10x + 9x - 15$

$2x(3x - 5) + 3(3x - 5)$

$(2x + 3)(3x - 5)$

This is the original binomial product. Note that it does not matter what binomial is listed first in this product, as $(a)(b) = (b)(a)$.

Example 2

Factor $6x^3 - 3x^2 - 3x$.

Solution

First, remove any common factors $(3x)$: $(3x)(2x^2 - x - 1)$.

Now, work with the trinomial using decomposition, remembering to include the $3x$ in the final answer.

$2x^2 - x - 1$

$(a)(b) = (2)(-1) = -2$

$(-2)(1) = -2$

$(-2) + (1) = b$

$2x^2 - 2x + x - 1$ (middle term decomposed)

$2x(x - 1) + 1(x - 1)$ (grouping)

$(2x + 1)(x - 1)$

The final factored answer is $(3x)(2x + 1)(x - 1)$.

SUPPLEMENTAL MATERIAL

Using the skills presented in this chapter, it is possible to solve many additional factoring problems, even if they appear slightly different than usual.

Examples and lessons covered so far have described the ideas of descending order of degree terms, as well as factoring out a common factor. Use these skills to solve the following example.

Example 3

Factor $6 + \dfrac{7}{2}x + \dfrac{x^2}{2}$.

This trinomial is written in ascending order. In general, any simplification or factoring should be put into the now familiar descending order:

$$\frac{1}{2}x^2 + \frac{7}{2}x + 6$$

As well, there are fractional numerical coefficients here, which is new but not something difficult to deal with.

Factor out a common factor of $\dfrac{1}{2}$ from each term.

Solution

$$\left(\frac{1}{2}\right)(x^2 + 7x + 12)$$

$$\left(\frac{1}{2}\right)(x^2 + 3x + 4x + 12)$$

$$\left(\frac{1}{2}\right)(x(x+3) + 4(x+3))$$

$$\left(\frac{1}{2}\right)(x+4)(x+3)$$

You can use either the inspection method or decomposition (shown here).

The skills needed to factor out a fraction, are not reviewed here. Emphasis should be placed on the fact that the constant term changes from 6 to 12 when the $\dfrac{1}{2}$ factor is removed.

PRACTICE EXERCISES

1. The decomposition method suggests that the middle term of the polynomial $\left(x^2 + 5x - 36\right)$ be broken down into two terms whose coefficients
    A. add to 5 and multiply to -36
    B. add to 5 and multiply to 36
    C. are both negative
    D. are both positive

2. A student is using decomposition to factor a trinomial. The leading coefficient is 6, the product of the constant and the leading coefficient is 12, and the middle term to be broken down has a numerical coefficient of 7.
    a) What was the original trinomial?

    b) Factor the original trinomial.

3. In order to factor $3m^2 - 13m + 12$, the middle term must be broken down to
    A. $-13m, -1m$
    B. $-9m, -4m$
    C. $3m, 12m$
    D. two equal terms

4. List all the possible values for a and b that make $(a)(b) = -120$. Then, isolate the pair that also makes $a + b = 7$.

5. Factor $6y^2 + 7y - 20$ by using the information from question 4 to assist with decomposition.

6. A student is given a list of terms that are to be added and subtracted. The student knows that after simplifying and factoring by decomposition, the final result is $(2x + 3)(5x + 4)$.

However, the student accidentally erased one of the terms on the list. Fill in the missing term below.

$$4x^2 - 2x + x^2 - x^3 + 5x^2 + 6 + x^3 + \underline{\hspace{1cm}} + 6$$

Lesson 8   DIVISION OF A POLYNOMIAL

In this lesson, skills will be developed to allow for a polynomial to be divided by a constant, a monomial, and certain binomials.
To begin, consider the following terms and ideas associated with division.

Given the long division: $5\overline{)20}$ with quotient 4

The term being divided (20) is known as the **dividend**.

The term that it is being divided by (5) is called the **divisor**.

The result of the division (4) is called the **quotient**.

Note that since there is not a remainder, the dividend and quotient are factors of the dividend.

In this case, when the number 20 is divided by 5 the result is 4, with nothing left over. If there were any amount left over, it would be called the **remainder**. To check the division, multiply the quotient by the divisor, $(5)(4) = 20$. This is correct, and there is no remainder.

Dividend = Quotient × Divisor + Remainder

Example 1

Divide 21 by 5.

Solution

Using long division:
$$5\overline{)21}$$
$$\underline{20}$$
$$1$$
The 1 left over is the remainder.

Long division is only briefly reviewed here, as the skills should be known. Also, not all steps in the long division process will always be shown in the examples.

In the example above, it could be stated that $21 = (5)(4) + 1$.

The division process can be applied to polynomials. Division is expressed mathematically in the following way:

$$\frac{polynomial}{divisor} = quotient + \frac{remainder}{divisor}$$

$$\frac{P}{D} = Q + \frac{R}{D}$$

To check for accuracy the expression becomes:

$$polynomial = (divisor)(quotient) + remainder$$
$$P = DQ + R$$

Example 2

Divide the polynomial $(y^2 - y + 6)$ by $(y + 2)$.

Solution

Set up the division as follows:

$$
\begin{array}{r}
y - 3 \\
y + 2 \overline{)\, y^2 - y - 6} \\
-(y^2 + 2y) \\
\hline
-3y - 6 \\
-(-3y - 6) \\
\hline
0
\end{array}
$$

- y^2 divided by y is y. Put this in the quotient.
- $y(y + 2)$ is $y^2 + 2y$. Subtract this from the dividend.
- $-3y$ divided by y is -3. Put this in the quotient.
- $-3(y + 2)$ is $-3y - 6$. Subtract this from the previous answer.

NOTES

Here, there is no remainder. The statement of the division can be stated as:

$$\frac{y^2 - y - 6}{y + 2} = (y - 3) + \frac{remainder}{y + 2}$$

$$\frac{y^2 - y - 6}{y + 2} = y - 3$$

Writing in the minus sign and brackets is helpful to help you to remember to subtract all terms.

The statement of the division could also be:

$$y^2 - y - 6 = (y + 2)(y - 3) + remainder$$

$$y^2 - y - 6 = (y + 2)(y - 3)$$

Example 3

Divide $4 - 8x + 12x^2$ by 2.

Solution

First, with its terms in descending order rewrite the polynomial.

$$
\begin{array}{r}
6x^2 - 4x + 2 \\
2 \overline{)\, 12x^2 - 8x + 4} \\
12x^2 \\
\hline
0 - 8x \\
-8x \\
\hline
0 + 4 \\
+4 \\
\hline
0
\end{array}
$$

The remainder here is 0. The quotient is $6x^2 - 4x + 2$. A full division statement could be given in either of the two forms already shown.

DIVISION OF POLYNOMIALS WITH A ZERO COEFFICIENT TERM

Some division questions present a polynomial where one or more of the numerical coefficients are zero, and hence not present.

Example 4

Divide $\left(6x^3 - 7x - 1\right)$ by $(x-1)$.

Solution

The missing x^2 term must be added to the polynomial in order for long division to produce a correct answer. This is accomplished by adding a $0x^2$ term (so as not to change the actual value of the expression).
The division is dealt with as follows:

$$
\begin{array}{r}
6x^2 + 6x - 1 \\
x-1\overline{\smash{)}6x^3 + 0x^2 - 7x - 1} \\
\underline{6x^3 - 6x^2} \\
+6x^2 - 7x \\
\underline{6x^2 - 6x} \\
-x - 1 \\
\underline{-x + 1} \\
-2
\end{array}
$$

Now, there is a remainder, so the two ways of expressing the division statement are:

$$\frac{6x^3 + 6x - 1}{x-1} = (6x^2 + 6x - 1) + \frac{(-2)}{x-1}$$

and

$$6x^3 + 6x - 1 = (x-1)(6x^2 + 6x - 1) + (-2)$$

For each of the expressions above, the last term (the remainder term) could have its brackets removed by applying the negative appropriately into the expression. Also, note that when the original polynomial is expressed in either statement, it is written as it originally appears, without the added $0x^2$ term. This term is added only for the long division.

DIVISION OF A POLYNOMIAL BY A BINOMIAL WITH A LEADING COEFFICIENT THAT IS NOT 1

The process of long division does not change if the divisor is a binomial with a leading coefficient that is not 1. This is shown by the next example.

Example 5

Simplify $\dfrac{2x^2 - 2}{2x - 2}$.

Solution

Set up as long division, and remember to include the missing $0x$ term.

$$
\begin{array}{r}
x + 1 \\
2x - 2 \enclose{longdiv}{2x^2 + 0x - 2} \\
\underline{2x^2 - 2x} \\
2x - 2 \\
\underline{2x - 2} \\
0
\end{array}
$$

When simplified, $\dfrac{2x^2 - 2}{2x - 2} = x + 1$.

DIVISION OF A POLYNOMIAL BY A SECOND DEGREE BINOMIAL

Sometimes, the divisor takes the form $ax^2 + c$. In this case, it is not necessary to insert a $0x^2$ term into the divisor. This is only done when the original polynomial has zero numerical coefficients.

Example 6

Find the quotient and remainder, and write one of the division statements for the following:

$$\left(4x^3 - 2x^2 - x - 1\right) \div \left(2x^2 + 1\right)$$

$$
\begin{array}{r}
2x - 1 \\
2x^2 + 1 \enclose{longdiv}{4x^3 - 2x^2 - x - 1} \\
\underline{4x^3 \qquad + 2x} \\
-2x^2 - 3x - 1 \\
\underline{-2x^2 \qquad -1} \\
-3x
\end{array}
$$

Note that in the blank space areas, a zero coefficient term could be shown. As long as the terms are lined up properly (i.e., proper long division technique), the answer should be correct. Here, the division process is stopped at the point when the dividend can no longer divide into the remaining expression. Hence, the term remainder.

Solution

Quotient: $2x - 1$

Remainder: $-3x$

Division statement:

$$\frac{4x^3 - 2x^2 - x - 1}{2x^2 + 1} = 2x - 1 + \frac{(-3x)}{2x^2 + 1}$$

$$\frac{polynomial}{divisor} = quotient + \frac{remainder}{divisor}$$

or

$$4x^3 - 2x^2 - x - 1 = (2x^2 + 1)(2x - 1) + (-3x)$$
$$4x^3 - 2x^2 - x - 1 = (2x^2 + 1)(2x - 1) - 3x$$

$$polynomial = (divisor)(quotient) + remainder$$

112

PRACTICE EXERCISES

1. Divide $24m^3 + 12m^2 + 6m$ by $6m$ (trinomial divided by monomial).

2. Divide $\left(x^3 + 5x^2 + 10x - 15\right)$ by $(x - 3)$ (polynomial divided by binomial).

    Express the answer in the form $\dfrac{polynomial}{divisor} = quotient + \dfrac{remainder}{divisor}$.

3. Find the original polynomial whose quotient is $5x - 1$, divisor is $x + 3$, and remainder is 3.

4. If the area of a particular rectangle is represented by the expression $x^2 - 5x - 36$ and the width is represented as $x - 9$ cm, then what is the expression that represents the length of the rectangle?

5. What is a polynomial that, when divided by $2x$, the remainder is 23?

REVIEW SUMMARY

In this unit, you have learned how to . . .

- factor a difference of squares, including cases that have a greatest common factor, in the form $a^2x^2 - b^2y^2$, where a may or may not be a factor of b

- factor single variable trinomials, including cases that require decomposition, in the form $ax^2 + bx + c$, where a may or may not be a factor of b and c

- find the product of polynomials, including the product of three binomials, as well as a binomial and a trinomial

- divide polynomials by binomials, where the divisor is in the form $(x - b)$, $(ax - b)$, or $(ax^2 - b)$

- express the results of dividing polynomials by binomials with division statements of the form $\frac{P}{D} = Q + \frac{R}{D}$ and $P = DQ + R$

PRACTICE TEST

1. Given the polynomial $x^2y + 2x - z^2$, state the degree of each term and the variables involved.

2. Simplify $(1-x)(2-x^2)$. Write the terms in descending order.

    $2 - 3x$

3. How many different factors does $8x$ have?
    A. 1
    B. 4
    C. 8
    D. 16

4. Find the GCF for $25x^2yz + 50xy^2z - 100xyz^2$.

    $5(5x^2yz + 10xy^2z - 20xyz^2)$

5. Factor $2x^2 + 13x + 15$.

    $(2x + 15)(x + 1)$ $(2x + 15)(x + 1)$

    $2x^2 + 15x - 2x - 15$ $2x^2 + 15x + 2x$

    $2x^2 \ 13x - 15$ $(2x - 1)(x + 15)$

                                $2x^2 - 1x + 30$

6. What is the value of a in $4x^2 - (3a)^2$ if this difference of squares factors to $(2x + 15)(2x - 15)$?

7. If $(x^3 + 1)(x^a - 1) = x^6 - 1$, what is the value of a?

8. To apply the decomposition method when factoring $x^2 - 8x - 9$, find two numbers that add to a and multiply to b. When a is subtracted from b, the result is _____.

9. Given that there is no remainder in the problem $y+3 \overline{)\ x\ }^{\displaystyle y+4}$, solve for the unknown dividend, x.

10. Show all long division steps to solve the problem $\left(2x^3 - x^2 - 2x + 2\right) \div \left(2x - 1\right)$. What would the original polynomial have to be to produce **no** remainder?

RATIONAL EXPRESSIONS

When you are finished this unit, you should be able to . . .

- reduce single-variable rational expressions containing monomials, binomials, and trinomials
- determine non-permissible values for single-variable rational expressions
- multiply single-variable rational expressions
- divide single-variable rational expressions
- add single-variable rational expressions
- subtract single-variable rational expressions
- find and verify solutions to rational equations

Lesson	Page	Completed on
1. Introduction to Rational Expressions and Non-Permissible Values	120	
2. Simplifying Rational Expressions	126	
3. Multiplying Rational Expressions	131	
4. Dividing Rational Expressions	137	
Practice Quiz	144	
5. Addition and Subtraction of Rational Expressions	146	
6. Rational Equations and Problem Solving	153	
Review Summary	161	
Practice Test	162	
Answers and Solutions	at the back of the book	

PREREQUISITE SKILLS AND KNOWLEDGE

Prior to beginning this unit, you should be able to . . .

- reduce fractions
- add, subtract, multiply, and divide fractions
- factor binomials and trinomials
- solve single-variable equations
- translate word problems into algebraic expressions

Lesson 1   *INTRODUCTION TO RATIONAL EXPRESSIONS AND NON-PERMISSIBLE VALUES*

A rational number is any number that can be written as a fraction, with the following restrictions placed on the fraction: the numerator and denominator must both be integers, and the denominator cannot equal zero. If these restrictions are not met, the number is not a rational number.

For example, consider the numbers $4, 5\frac{1}{2}, -3.5$. Each of these can be expressed as an equivalent fraction as follows: $\frac{4}{1}, \frac{11}{2}, -\frac{7}{2}$.

Each of the equivalent fractions is rational, as none of them conflicts with the stated restrictions.

A rational expression is a quotient of polynomials. Restrictions are placed on the polynomials, just as restrictions were placed on the numerator and denominator of the rational number fraction. In the case of a rational expression, neither polynomial can contain variables with a fractional degree (a variable in a radical) or a variable degree (a variable in the exponent).

Example 1

Consider each of the following expressions. Determine which ones are and which ones are not rational expressions.

a) $\dfrac{2x^2 - 1}{2x + 1}$

> *Solution*
>
> This is a quotient of polynomials and the exponent of each of the variables is an integer, so this is a rational expression.

b) $x^4 + x + 3$

> *Solution*
>
> Although at first glance this does not appear to be a quotient, it can be expressed in the form of a fraction as
>
> $$\dfrac{x^4 + x + 3}{1}$$
>
> This is a quotient of polynomials, with integral exponents. So, this is a rational expression.

120

NOTES

c) $\dfrac{x^{\frac{1}{3}} + \sqrt{x}}{x + 3^x}$

Solution

This is a quotient, but the exponents do not obey the restrictions. In the numerator, the polynomial has a term with degree $\dfrac{1}{3}$ and another term of degree $\dfrac{1}{2}$. Also, the denominator has a term with a variable degree (x). This is not a rational expression.

NON-PERMISSIBLE VALUES

A rational expression is the quotient of two polynomials and, as a quotient, the value of the expression becomes undefined if the denominator becomes equal to zero. The values of a variable that cause the denominator to equal zero are called non-permissible values.

The expression "non-permissible values" is used, even if there is only one non-permissible value.

Example 2

When is the following rational expression undefined? In other words, what are the non-permissible values?

$\dfrac{25a + 4}{2a}$

The denominator would equal zero if $a = 0$. This rational expression is undefined when $a = 0$. The non-permissible value for a is zero.

In some cases (as in the example above), the non-permissible values are easy to identify. In other cases, the polynomial in the denominator may have to be factored to identify the non-permissible values. It should also be stated here that many rational expressions have no non-permissible values, as they are defined for all values of the variables.

Example 3

Identify the non-permissible values, if any are present, for the following expressions:

$\dfrac{x - 3}{23}$

$\dfrac{23}{x - 3}$

Solution

The first rational expression is placed here as a reminder that non-permissible values are found when the denominator equals zero. Values that produce a zero numerator are not of concern. In the first rational expression, the numerator will equal zero if $x - 3 = 0$, or $x = 3$. This results in $\dfrac{0}{23}$ or just 0.

This is permissible.

In the second rational expression, the denominator will equal zero when $x = 3$. (We know this by solving the equation $x - 3 = 0$.)

The non-permissible value for x in the second rational expression is 3.

Example 4

State any non-permissible values for the variable in each of the following rational expressions.

$$\frac{2x + 1}{x^2 - x - 2}$$

$$\frac{2x + 1}{x^2 - 4}$$

$$\frac{2x + 1}{x^2 + 1}$$

Solution

For the first rational expression, the denominator can be factored to produce the equivalent rational expression $\dfrac{2x + 1}{(x - 2)(x + 1)}$.

The denominator will be equal to zero if either of the two factors becomes zero. That is, if $(x - 2) = 0$ or if $(x + 1) = 0$.

Solving these two equations gives the resulting non-permissible values for the first rational expression as $x = 2, -1$.

There are a number of different ways of stating the non-permissible values for a rational expression. The first way is to state, as above, that the non-permissible values for the variable are $x = 2, -1$. The second way does not include the term "non-permissible" in a sentence, but rather states $x \neq 2, -1$. Other ways shorten the terminology of "non-permissible values" to NPV and state either NPV for $x = 2, -1$ or sometimes simply NPV $= 2, -1$.

For the second rational expression, the denominator can be solved to find when the variable will equal zero.

$$x^2 - 4 = 0$$
$$x^2 = 4$$
$$x = \pm\sqrt{4}$$
$$x = \pm 2$$

The non-permissible values for the variable x in this rational expression are $\pm\sqrt{4}$. Note the importance of retaining both the positive and negative square root.

For the third rational expression, any non-permissible values would result from solving the equation (denominator) $x^2 + 1 = 0$ or $x^2 = -1$. There are no real numbers that can produce this result for the variable, so there are no non-permissible values.

NOTES

Note that if the equation were $x \times \sqrt{4}$, your answer would only include the positive 2.

PRACTICE EXERCISES

1. Which of the following expressions is a rational expression?

   A. $\dfrac{\sqrt{x}}{y}$

   B. $\dfrac{2x}{\sqrt{2x}}$

   C. $\dfrac{24}{x^{\frac{3}{2}}}$

   D. $\sqrt[3]{x} + \sqrt[3]{8}$

2. Which of the following expressions is **not** a rational expression?

   A. $\dfrac{x-1}{x^2}$

   B. $\dfrac{1-x}{x^{(2+2)}}$

   C. $\dfrac{1}{x^{3x}}$

   D. $2x + 7$

3. Write the equation(s) required to evaluate when the numerators, and when the denominators, equal zero for the following expressions.

   a) $\dfrac{(x+2)(2x)}{3(x-2)(x)}$

   b) $\dfrac{5(x^2-1)}{(x^2-4)}$

4. Solve the equations in question 3 above, and state which of the solutions indicate non-permissible values.

5. List any non-permissible values for the variable in the expression $\dfrac{x+6}{(x^2-36)}$.

6. List any non-permissible values for the expression $\dfrac{2+3x}{2(x+2)(x^2+5x+6)}$.

Lesson 2 SIMPLIFYING RATIONAL EXPRESSIONS

NOTES

Rational expressions are not always found in their most simplified, or reduced, form. There may be terms common to both the numerator and denominator that can be eliminated. In order to see if there are any common terms, it is often necessary to factor the numerator and denominator.

The simplest reduction of a rational expression involves factoring a constant out of the numerator and denominator, separately, and then reducing the expression.

Note that you cannot simply cancel out the $\frac{2x}{2x}$ or the $\frac{2}{-2}$ because these are not monomials.

Example 1

Factor and reduce the following expression.

$$\frac{2x+2}{2x-2}$$

Solution

Both terms in the numerator and the denominator have a common factor of 2. Rewrite this, as follows, and divide through by 2 in the numerator and denominator to remove (cancel out) the common factor.

$$\frac{2(x+1)}{2(x-1)}$$

$$\frac{x+1}{x-1}$$

This resulting rational expression is equivalent to the initial expression. Both the initial and final rational expressions are said to be **equivalent forms**. The difference in the two forms is that the final form has had a common factor removed from both the numerator and denominator.
It is a simplified (reduced) form. If all common factors (constants and variables) are factored out and cancelled, the final equivalent form is called the simplest form.

The non-permissible values for the rational expression above can be found when the denominator is zero.

$$2x-2=0$$
$$2x=2$$
$$x=1$$

$$x-1=0$$
$$x=1$$

The non-permissible value is $x=1$ (found from either the unsimplified or simplified expression).

It is important to use the unsimplified expression to determine non-permissible values. In this case, the value is the same, but if the simplification (reduction) process involves variables, it is possible to lose non-permissible values. This is illustrated in Example 2.

Example 2

Factor the numerator and denominator fully and determine any common terms in the following expression. Simplify the expression by cancelling those terms (noting the non-permissible values at each step).

$$\frac{4x^2}{2x}$$

Solution

Factoring fully yields $\dfrac{(4)(x)(x)}{(2)(x)}$, with the single non-permissible value of $x = 0$.

The 4 in the numerator could have been expressed as $(2)(2)$, but this simplification is not necessary. Dividing both the numerator and the denominator by 2 and x produces the following simplified (reduced) rational expression.

$$\frac{2x}{1} \text{ or just } 2x$$

This reduced form has no non-permissible values, but the initial rational expression did have the stated non-permissible value of $x = 0$. It is necessary to state any non-permissible value that occurs at any step along the simplification process.

In Example 1, a common factor of a constant was removed to simplify the expression. In Example 2, a constant and a variable was removed.
In more complex rational expressions, it may be necessary to remove a factor involving a variable $\pm$ a constant.

In this example, $2x$ was divided out of both the numerator and denominator, reducing the expression to a more simplified form. This is referred to as cancelling a $2x$ from the numerator and denominator. This terminology can be used so long as it is clear that the term being cancelled does not entirely disappear; it leaves a value of 1 in its place.

Example 3

Express the following rational expression in its simplest form. State any NPVs.

$$\frac{3x + 6}{2x + 4}$$

Solution

Factor completely and cancel common factors:

$$\frac{3(x + 2)}{2(x + 2)}$$

$$\frac{3}{2}$$

$$2x + 4 = 0$$
$$x = -2$$

The simplest form of the given rational expression is $\frac{3}{2}$ and the non-permissible value is $x = -2$.

Factoring completely before cancelling helps eliminate common cancelling mistakes. A common mistake is illustrated below.

$$\frac{2x + 1}{2x}$$

$$\frac{2\!\!\!/x + 1}{2\!\!\!/x}\qquad\textbf{Incorrect cancelling}$$

$$1$$

In the expression above, the $2x$ cannot be cancelled because it is not a common factor of the numerator. There is a $+1$ term that does not have a $2x$ that can be factored out.

PRACTICE EXERCISES

1. What are all the non-permissible values of x for the expression $\dfrac{(x+1)(x+2)}{(x+1)(x+3)}$?

   A. $x = 1, 3$
   B. $x = 3$
   C. $x = -1, -3$
   D. $x = 1, 2, 3$

2. Reduce the following expression if possible, stating any restrictions on the variable.

   $\dfrac{3x^2 - 1}{x}$

3. Express the following expression in its simplest form and state any non-permissible values for the variable.

   $\dfrac{(x-2)}{(x^2 + x - 6)}$

4. Completely reduce the following expression and state any NPVs.

   $\dfrac{x-1}{(x^2 - 1)}$

5. Which of the following expressions is equivalent to $(1-x)$?

   A. $(x-1)$

   B. $(1+x)(1-x)$

   C. $-(x-1)$

   D. $-(x+1)$

6. Reduce the following expression to its simplest form, stating restrictions on the variable.

$$\frac{18-50y^2}{20y+12}$$

7. A particular volume of gas is described by the polynomial $x^3 + 2x^2$. The gas is confined within a cube, which has a width of $x+2$ units. Write a rational expression that describes, in simplest terms, the ratio of the gas volume per unit of space. What are the restrictions on the variable x?

Lesson 3 *MULTIPLYING RATIONAL EXPRESSIONS*

Multiplication of rational expressions is accomplished by multiplying all factors in the first numerator by all factors in the consequent numerator(s). In a similar fashion, all factors in each denominator are multiplied.

All factors originally in any numerator form the new numerator, and all factors originally in a denominator form the new denominator.

Example 1

Multiply the given rational expression.

$$\frac{1}{2} \bullet \frac{4}{7}$$

Solution

$$\frac{1}{2} \times \frac{4}{7}$$

$$\frac{4}{14}$$

$$\frac{2}{7}$$

The terms in each numerator have been multiplied, and the terms in the denominator have as well. After the multiplication is complete, the expression was reduced by removing a common factor of 2 .

Rational expressions can be simplified by factoring and cancelling common factors. When two or more rational expressions are to be multiplied, cancelling can be performed between any common factors in the numerator and denominator, regardless of which numerator or denominator they are found in. This is a result of the fact that after multiplication, all the factors in each numerator will form a new common numerator. All factors in each denominator will also form the new denominator.

From the previous example, $\dfrac{1}{2} \times \dfrac{4}{7} = \dfrac{1}{\cancel{2}_1} \times \dfrac{\cancel{4}^2}{7} = \dfrac{2}{7}$

Example 2

Factor each numerator and denominator in the following rational expressions. Multiply, and then cancel any common factors.

$$\frac{x^2 + 2x}{3x} \times \frac{9x}{x+2}$$

$\dfrac{1}{2} \bullet \dfrac{4}{7}$ is equivalent to $\dfrac{1}{2} \times \dfrac{4}{7}$ or $\left(\dfrac{1}{2}\right)\left(\dfrac{4}{7}\right)$

The dot, $\bullet$, to represent multiplication, is employed since x is a variable.

Brackets can also be avoided by using this notation.

NOTES

Solution

$$\frac{(x)(x+2)}{(3)(x)} \times \frac{(3)(3)(x)}{(x+2)}$$

$$\frac{(3)(3)(x)(x)(x+2)}{(3)(x)(x+2)}$$

$$\frac{3x}{1}$$

$$3x$$

The example did not specifically ask for any non-permissible values, but even so, it is important to list them with the solution. When do the original denominators equal zero?

$$3x = 0$$

$$x = 0$$

$$x + 2 = 0$$

$$x = -2$$

Therefore, the non-permissible values for x are 0 and -2.

In Example 2, the instructions stated that cancelling needed to be performed only after multiplication. It is often more efficient to simplify the multiplication process by cancelling common factors initially and then multiplying. More cancelling can then occur if necessary.

Cancelling common terms before multiplication simplifies the resulting rational expression. It also prevents the following mistake (the last step):

$$\frac{(x)(x+2)}{(3)(x)} \times \frac{(3)(3)(x)}{(x+2)}$$

$$\frac{(3)(3)(x)(x)(x+2)}{(3)(x)(x+2)}$$

$$\frac{9x^3 + 18x^2}{3x^2 + 6x}$$

At this point, the numerator and denominator will have to be factored again, and common terms cancelled. This is unnecessary additional work.

Example 3

Multiply the rational expressions given in Example 2. Cancel any common terms, find any NPVs, and compare the results.

Solution

$$\frac{x^2 + 2x}{3x} \times \frac{9x}{x+2}$$

$$\frac{(x)(x+2)}{(3)(x)} \times \frac{(3)(3)(x)}{(x+2)}$$

$$\frac{3x}{1}$$

$$3x$$

The common factors of $(3), (x)$, and $(x+2)$ were cancelled before the multiplication, giving the result shown. From the initial denominators, the NPVs are $x = 0, -2$. The answers are identical to those in Example 2.

Example 4

Multiply the following rational expressions and note any restrictions on the variable.

$$\frac{2x}{x} \times \frac{3}{x} \times \frac{(x+1)}{2} \qquad \frac{\cancel{2}\cancel{x}}{\cancel{x}} \times \frac{3}{x} \times \frac{(x+1)}{\cancel{2}} \qquad \text{Show cancelling.}$$

Solution

$$\frac{3(x+1)}{x}$$

$$x \neq 0$$

The example above illustrates that the multiplication process can be applied to more than two rational expressions. Additionally, even though common factors of x were cancelled in the multiplication process, the restrictions on the variable found by examining the original denominators are the same as the restrictions on the final expression.

PRACTICE EXERCISES

1. Multiplying the following expressions, expressing the final rational expression in its simplest form. State any restrictions on the variable.

$$\frac{(x+1)^3}{24x} \times \frac{6(2x)}{2x^2 - 2}$$

2. Solve the following multiplication problem and state any NPVs.

$$\left(\frac{3(x+1)^2}{4(x-1)^2} \right) \left(\frac{4(x+1)^2}{3(x-1)^2} \right)$$

3. Which of the following expressions is equivalent to $\frac{3}{x}$?

    A. $\frac{2}{3} \times \frac{6}{x}$

    B. $\frac{3}{x} \times 2$

    C. $-\frac{x}{4x^2} \times -\frac{12x}{x}$

    D. $-\left(\frac{x}{3} \right)$

4. Multiply the following rational expressions. State the answer in the most reduced form and list all NPVs.

$$\left(\frac{x^2 - 4}{x^2 + 5x - 14} \right)\left(\frac{2x^2 + 14x}{2} \right)$$

5. The rational expression $\dfrac{2}{x}$ is found as the result of multiplying two or more complex rational expressions (and reducing). State two rational expressions that could give this result, and state any NPVs for these rational expressions.

6. Perform the same task as that in question 5, but in this case, the restrictions on the variable must include $x \neq 4$.

7. For the expression $\dfrac{(x+1)(x+2)(x+3)...(x+n)}{1} \cdot \dfrac{1}{(x+1)(x+2)....(x+n-1)}$, it is true that

    A. there are n non-permissible values

    B. after cancelling, the denominator becomes zero

    C. after cancelling, the numerator becomes $(x + n)$

    D. the problem cannot be solved

Lesson 4   DIVIDING RATIONAL EXPRESSIONS

One rational expression divided by another can be expressed as the first expression **multiplied** by the reciprocal of the second expression.

To understand why this is true, consider the following examples.

Example 1

Use the procedure stated above to solve the following division of rational expressions.

$$\frac{x^2}{2} \div \frac{x^2}{2}$$

Solution

$$\frac{x^2}{2} \div \frac{x^2}{2}$$

$$\frac{x^2}{2} \times \frac{2}{x^2} \qquad \text{Multiply by the reciprocal.}$$

$$\frac{2x^2}{2x^2}$$

$$1$$

$$x \neq 0$$

Conceptually, this makes sense since the first expression is being divided by itself (an identical expression). Any number divided by itself is 1
(with the exception of 0). Any variable divided by itself is 1
(with the restriction that the variable cannot equal 0).

Example 2

Consider the following division of fractions.

$$1 \div \frac{1}{2}$$

Solution

$$\frac{1}{1} \div \frac{1}{2}$$

$$1 \times 2 = 2$$

Does it make sense that 1 divided by $\frac{1}{2}$ (divided into halves),

produces 2 ? A whole pizza, if cut in half (divided by $\frac{1}{2}$),

produces two separate halves.

DIVISION AND NON-PERMISSIBLE VALUES

Once a division of rational expressions is expressed as multiplication by the reciprocal, the steps to solve and simplify are unchanged. However, one more step is required to ensure that all non-permissible values are named. It is essential, as indicated in Lesson 3, to list all non-permissible values in the original expression. This is as a result of the fact that cancelling may cause some factors to "disappear."

When dividing, the denominator of each term must be examined for NPVs before changing the division to a multiplication. Additionally, any terms that are flipped to the reciprocal have new denominators that must also be examined. All NPVs must be listed for a complete answer.

Example 3

Solve and list restrictions on the variable for the following division problem.

$$\frac{2(x^2-9)}{3x} \div \frac{(x+3)}{2x}$$

Solution

$$\frac{2(x+3)(x-3)}{3x} \cdot \frac{2x}{(x+3)}$$

$$\frac{4(x-3)}{3}$$

$$3x = 0$$
$$x = 0$$
$$2x = 0$$
$$x = 0$$

$$3x = 0$$
$$x = 0$$
$$x + 3 = 0$$
$$x = -3$$

From the initial division statement, it was found that $x \neq 0$. This result was duplicated, once from each denominator. In the second step of the solution, the second expression was flipped (to its reciprocal) and the division now changed to multiplication. As a result, the new denominator contributed an additional restriction of $x \neq -3$. Both of these restrictions should be listed for the complete set of NPVs.

DIVISION STATEMENT

A rational expression divided by another rational expression can be expressed in the form shown in examples 1–3, or the division can take other forms.

Fractional form

$$\frac{\dfrac{x+1}{2x}}{\dfrac{x-1}{4x}}$$

In fractional form, it can be difficult to identify the correct original denominators and new denominator formed by the reciprocal. Rewriting this expression in the form shown in the previous examples is recommended before solving.

$$\frac{\dfrac{x+1}{2x}}{\dfrac{x-1}{4x}} \text{ can be rewritten as } \frac{x+1}{2x} \div \frac{x-1}{4x}$$

This can now be solved using the methods demonstrated in this lesson and in lesson 3.

Written form

The division statement may be contained within a word problem, and in this case, the rational expressions must be written out as stated within the word problem.

"A quotient is found by dividing $\dfrac{x+1}{2x}$ by a second rational expression. The second rational expression has a numerator of $x-1$ and a denominator of $4x$. What is the final simplified result?"

This question is simply a written form of the previous question. The solution will be the same.

Example 4

Rewrite the following expression by removing the fractional form. Simplify and state all restrictions on the variable.

$$\frac{\dfrac{(x^2 - x - 42)}{(x^4 - 1)}}{\dfrac{(x - 7)}{(x - 1)^2}}$$

Solution

$$\frac{(x - 7)(x + 6)}{\left(x^2 + 1\right)\left(x^2 - 1\right)} \div \frac{(x - 7)}{(x - 1)^2} \quad \text{write as } (x - 1)(x - 1)$$

$$\frac{(\cancel{x - 7})(x + 6)}{\left(x^2 + 1\right)(x + 1)(\cancel{x - 1})} \times \frac{(\cancel{x - 1})(x - 1)}{(\cancel{x - 7})}$$

$$\frac{(x + 6)(x - 1)}{\left(x^2 + 1\right)(x + 1)}$$

This is fully simplified. To find any restrictions on the variable, examine the denominators in each step.

Note that the denominator factor $(x^2 + 1)$ has no real NPVs.

$$(x^2 - 1) = 0$$
$$x = \pm 1$$

The restriction $x \neq \pm 1$ is repeated but only needs to be listed once.

$$(x - 7) = 0$$
$$x = 7$$

So, all the restrictions are that $x \neq -1, 1, 7$.

PRACTICE EXERCISES

1. Simplify the expression $\dfrac{5}{\left(\dfrac{20}{x^2}\right)}$.

2. A triangle has an area defined by the formula of base times height divided by 2. If the base is represented by the expression $x^2 - 2x + 1$ and the height is represented the expression $\left(\dfrac{2x}{x-1}\right)^2$, what is the area of the triangle in simplified form? State any restrictions on the variable.

3. Which of the following expressions makes the equation $\dfrac{x}{3} \div y = \dfrac{2}{x}$ true?

   A. $y = \dfrac{x^2}{6}$

   B. $y = \dfrac{6}{x}$

   C. $y = \dfrac{x}{2}$

   D. $y = \dfrac{2x}{3x}$

4. Simplify and state the non-permissible values for the following expression.

$$\frac{x^2 - x - 12}{x + 1} \div \frac{x^2 - 5x + 4}{x^2 - 1}$$

5. Solve and reduce the following expression, stating all NPVs.

$$\frac{\dfrac{4(1 - x)}{x}}{\dfrac{x - 1}{2x}}$$

6. What is the value for b that will make the given division of rational expressions result in a simplified form of $2x$? State all NPVs.

$$\frac{25 - x^2}{bx} \div \frac{(5 + x)}{2b} \div \frac{(x - 5)}{-(bx - 1)} \times \frac{x^2}{(bx - 1)}$$

7. Which of the following statements about rational expressions is false?
   A. Restricted values are found only in denominators.
   B. Simplifying eliminates NPVs.
   C. Factors that are common to the numerator and denominator can be cancelled.
   D. If there are no variables, a fraction can still be undefined.

PRACTICE QUIZ

1. Which of the following statements is true?

   A. $\dfrac{2(x+1)}{2x-2}$ has the same NPVs as $\dfrac{x+1}{x-1}$.

   B. $\dfrac{3+x}{\sqrt{x}}$ is a rational expression.

   C. $x+5$ is not a rational expression.

   D. Only variables produce non-permissible values.

2. Three times a number is divided by the number minus 1. The result is then divided by the number minus 1. If the number is 2, what is the final result? Show how this question can be solved with rational expressions to obtain the final result. Additionally, what would not be an acceptable number to begin with?

3. The expression $\dfrac{(1+x)(2+x)}{(3+x)}$ can be simplified to

   A. 1

   B. $\dfrac{(1+x)}{2}$

   C. It cannot be simplified.

   D. $\dfrac{2}{3}$

4. Simplify the expression $\dfrac{x^2+9x+18}{x-1}\times\dfrac{2(x-1)}{3}\div 2$.

5. In the expression $\dfrac{1}{(x+1)} \times \dfrac{2}{(x+2)} \times \dfrac{3}{(x+3)} \times \cdots \times \dfrac{10}{(x+10)}$, what are all the NPVs for the variable?

6. Simplify and state all the NPVs for the expression $\dfrac{x^3 + 7x^2 + 12x}{3x + 9} \times \dfrac{3^2}{\sqrt{x^2 - 2x + 1}}$.

7. What are the NPVs for the expression $\dfrac{x^2 + x}{(x-1)} \div \dfrac{(x-2)}{(x-2)^2} \div \dfrac{3}{x} \times \dfrac{(x+3)}{4}$?

    A. $x \ne 0, 1, 2$
    B. $x \ne 1, 2, -3$
    C. $x \ne 1, 2, 2$
    D. $x \ne 0, 1, 2, -3$

8. Simplify and state the non-permissible values for the expression

    $$\dfrac{x^2 - 3x - 4}{(2x)^2} \div \left(\dfrac{4x - 16}{8x} \times \dfrac{x^2 - 1}{x} \right) .$$

Lesson 5 ADDITION AND SUBTRACTION OF RATIONAL EXPRESSIONS

The process of adding and subtracting rational expressions involves finding a common denominator for each expression, writing an equivalent expression with that new denominator, and then adding or subtracting the expressions. Simplification may occur after addition or subtraction.

This process will be broken down into the individual steps and demonstrated by examples.

SIMPLIFY EXPRESSIONS

In order to add or subtract rational expressions, it is necessary to find a common denominator. If the common denominator found is the lowest common denominator, there will be less reducing to perform in later steps.

To find the lowest common denominator, the first step is to ensure that each rational expression involved is in its most simplified form.

Example 1

What is the lowest common denominator for the following two expressions?

$$\frac{(x^2-1)}{(x+1)} \qquad \frac{2x}{1}$$

Solution

Remember that $(x^2-1)=(x+1)(x-1)$.

The first rational expression can be simplified by factoring the numerator and cancelling common factors. This reduces it to $\frac{(x-1)}{1}$.

So, it turns out that both expressions have a common denominator of 1. No more work is required on the denominator.

It is important to continue noting the non-permissible values. The first rational expression has an NPV of $x \neq -1$. Even though simplification caused the denominator of this expression to disappear, the non-permissible value must be listed for accuracy.

COMMON DENOMINATORS

The process for finding common denominators for rational expressions is basically the same as finding common denominators for rational numbers. Basic review is not included here, but some examples are included to introduce variables and polynomial expressions as denominators.

The process of writing equivalent expressions is then reviewed, and finally, more complex rational expressions are examined.

Example 2

Multiply the following three rational expressions.

$(2x)$ (3) $(x+1)$

Solution

$(2x)(3)(x+1)$

$(6x)(x+1)$

$6x^2 + 6x$

Example 3

What is the lowest common denominator for the following rational expressions?

$\dfrac{1}{2x}$ $\dfrac{1}{3}$ $\dfrac{1}{(x+1)}$

Solution

The lowest common denominator is $(2x)(3)(x+1)$. This is the **lowest** common denominator because the three denominators have no terms in common.

EQUIVALENT EXPRESSIONS

Example 4

Write equivalent expressions as indicated below.

$\dfrac{2x}{3} = \dfrac{?}{6}$

Solution

The denominator on the right-hand side of the equation is twice that of the left hand side. So, the numerator on the right will be 2 times the left numerator. Thus, $? = 4x$.

$\dfrac{2x}{3} = \dfrac{4x}{6}$

Up to this point, the process of factoring and cancelling common factors has been used to simplify the expression. In order to find common denominators, it is often necessary to make an expression more complex.

NOTES

Example 5

Write an equivalent rational expression as indicated below.

$$\frac{2x}{3} = \frac{?}{3(x+1)}$$

Solution

The denominator on the right-hand side has been multiplied by a factor of $(x+1)$.

The numerator $2x$ must also be multiplied by this factor to produce an equivalent rational expression.

$$\frac{2x}{3} = \frac{2x(x+1)}{3(x+1)}$$

There are two things to note at this point:
1) Do not cancel the common factors of $(x+1)$ in the numerator and denominator. This would just return the expression to its original form.
2) The $2x$ will have to be distributed through the $(x+1)$ before any addition or subtraction can occur.

Once a common denominator has been identified, each rational expression involved must be converted into an equivalent expression with that common denominator.

Example 6

Find the lowest common denominator for the following expressions, and write each expression as an equivalent expression with that common denominator.

$$\frac{2x+6}{4x} \qquad \frac{x-1}{2(x+1)}$$

Solution

First, check to ensure that each expression is in its simplest form.
Note that a common factor of 2 can be cancelled from the first expression.

$$\frac{x+3}{2x} \qquad \frac{x-1}{2(x+1)}$$

Next, check to see if there are any common factors in the denominators. Here, each denominator has a common factor of 2.

To find the lowest common denominator, multiply all the factors involved in the denominator, but if there are repeated common factors (such as 2, here) only include it once in the multiplication.

The lowest common denominator is $(2)(x)(x+1)$. Now, write each of the rational expressions above as an equivalent expression with this denominator.

$$\frac{(x+3)}{(2)(x)} = \frac{?}{(2)(x)(x+1)}$$
$$? = (x+3)(x+1)$$
$$x \neq 0, -1$$

The new rational expression is $\dfrac{(x+3)(x+1)}{(2)(x)(x+1)}$

$$\frac{(x-1)}{(2)(x+1)} = \frac{?}{(2)(x)(x+1)}$$
$$? = (x-1)(x)$$
$$x \neq 0, -1$$

The new rational expression is $\dfrac{(x-1)(x)}{(2)(x)(x+1)}$

The solution is complete. Note that since the two expressions have the same (lowest common) denominator, they will have similar NPVs.

The only different NPVs will be produced from the original denominator of each individual expression before factoring/cancelling to simplify.

At this point, since each expression has a common denominator, the expressions could be added or subtracted (whatever is indicated) by performing the stated operation on the numerators and retaining the common denominator.

Some questions ask for the answer to be stated in simplest form. This is achieved by using the lowest common denominator and as a last step, checking to ensure that the expression cannot be further reduced. If the denominator used for the addition or subtraction is not the lowest common denominator, simplifying as a last step can also achieve this goal.

Example 7

Simplify and state the NPVs for the following expression.

$$\frac{x+2}{x^2 - 3x - 10} + \frac{3x^2}{2x}$$

Solution

$$\frac{(x+2)}{(x+2)(x-5)} + \frac{3x(x)}{(2)(x)}$$

In this first step, brackets have been added to indicate separate factors that show either common factors to be cancelled, possible NPVs in the denominator, or both.

$$\frac{1}{(x-5)} + \frac{3x}{2}$$

The expressions are now simplified and there are no common factors in the denominators, so the lowest common denominator will be $(2)(x-5)$. Do not forget to look back at the original denominators to list all the NPVs at the end.

$$\frac{(2)}{(2)(x-5)} + \frac{(3x)(x-5)}{2(x-5)}$$

Each of the expressions has been converted to an equivalent expression with the common denominator. Now, add across the numerators, retaining the common denominator.
At this point, the numerator on the second expression will be expanded and then the terms will be put into descending order of degree.

$$\frac{2 + (3x^2 - 15x)}{(2)(x-5)}$$

$$\frac{3x^2 - 15x + 2}{2(x-5)}$$

As a final step, check to see if this can be reduced.
The numerator will not factor into anything that will be a common factor with the denominator, so the question is in its simplest form. Now, state all the NPVs.

$$x + 2 = 0$$
$$x = -2$$
$$x - 5 = 0$$
$$x = 5$$
$$x = 0$$

The NPVs are $x \neq -2, 0, 5$.

PRACTICE EXERCISES

1. Perform the indicated operations and simplify the following expression.

$$\frac{2}{3x} + \frac{3x}{4} - 1$$

2. The equivalent rational expression for $\frac{(x+1)(x-1)}{12x^2}$, with a new denominator of $12x^2(2x)$, will have a new numerator of
   A. $2(x+1)(x-1)$
   B. $(x+1)(x-1)$
   C. an unknown value
   D. $2x(x^2-1)$

3. Solve the following expression for x.

$$\frac{9y}{4} - \frac{x}{2} = \frac{y}{4}$$

4. Simplify and state the NPVs for the following expression.

$$\frac{a+1}{(2a+2)} + \frac{a-1}{2(a+1)} - \frac{6}{a}$$

5. Simplify and state the non-permissible values for the following expression.

$$\frac{x^2 - 6x - 7}{x + 1} - \frac{2x + 12}{2x + 2} + \frac{x + 1}{x^2 - 1}$$

6. When the expression below is simplified to a single rational expression, what value of x will produce a numerator of -3?

$$\frac{2}{(1 - x)} + \frac{x - 1}{(x - 1)(x)} - \frac{3}{(x - 1)(x)}$$

Lesson 6 RATIONAL EQUATIONS AND PROBLEM SOLVING

Rational expressions can be solved when expressed as an equation. In these cases, the methods for simplifying expressions are instrumental in obtaining the actual value for the variable.

Example 1

a) Simplify the following rational expression.

$$\frac{1}{x} + \frac{2}{x}$$

Solution

Since the denominators are the same, the addition of the numerators produces the simplified form $\frac{3}{x}$.

b) Given the answer above, solve the following rational equation by observation.

$$\frac{1}{x} + \frac{2}{x} = \frac{3}{4}$$

Solution

By simplifying the left-hand side of the equation, the equation becomes $\frac{3}{x} = \frac{3}{4}$. By observation, the only value for x that makes this statement true is $x = 4$. The non-permissible value for the variable is 0.

In this case, the variable had one value, which was apparent with little simplification necessary. In more complex cases, a series of steps will assist in the process of solving rational equations.

Step 1

Remove all denominators from the equation by multiplying all terms by the lowest common multiple of the denominators.

Example 2

Find the lowest common multiple (LCM) of the denominators in the following rational equation. Multiply each term by that LCM, and cancel like factors, but do not solve further.

$$\frac{2}{x} + \frac{3}{2x} = \frac{4}{(x+1)}$$

Solution

The lowest common multiple of these denominators is $(x)(2)(x+1)$. Multiplying this throughout produces

$$\frac{2(x)(2)(x+1)}{x} + \frac{3(x)(2)(x+1)}{2x} = \frac{4(x)(2)(x+1)}{(x+1)}$$

Now, cancel like terms to remove all denominators.
$$4(x+1) + 3(x+1) = 8x$$

Note that simplification can occur before finding the LCM. Observe the following example.

Example 3

Find the LCM for the following rational expression without initial simplifying, and with simplification.

$$\frac{2x}{4x} + \frac{3}{(x+1)}$$

Example 3 is placed here to illustrate LCM simplifying. Steps 2 – 6 continue with the rational equation from Example 2.

Solution

Without initial simplification, the LCM is $4x(x+1)$. However, if the first expression is reduced by cancelling a common factor of $2x$, the expression becomes $\frac{1}{2} + \frac{3}{(x+1)}$. In this case, the LCM is $2(x+1)$.

If the rational expression is not simplified initially, then the final form will require simplification to be reduced fully.

Step 2

Remove all brackets by multiplying (distributing) as necessary.

Returning to Example 2, the process of finding the LCM and multiplying produced $4(x+1) + 3(x+1) = 8x$. Now, applying step 2 produces $4x + 4 + 3x + 3 = 8x$.

Step 3

Collect and combine like terms from both sides of the equal sign. This can be done by gathering all the variables on one side and all the constants on the other side of the equal sign, or by gathering all the terms to one side, making the equation $= 0$.

Collecting like terms from $4x + 4 + 3x + 3 = 8x$ as described in step 3 gives either of the following results:

$7x + 7 = 8x$

$7x + 7 - 7 = 8x - 7$

$7x = 8x - 7$

$7x - 8x = 8x - 7$

$-x = -7$

$7x + 7 = 8x$

$7x + 7 - (7x + 7) = 8x - (7x + 7)$

$0 = 8x - 7x - 7$

$0 = x - 7$

Step 4

Solve. If there is a coefficient on the variable (other than 1), divide through by that coefficient to arrive at a final value that makes the original rational equation true.

$-x = -7$

$\dfrac{-x}{-1} = \dfrac{-7}{-1}$

$x = 7$

$0 = x - 7$

$7 = x$

$x = 7$

Step 5

State any NPVs for the variable, and compare these to the solution obtained in step 4). Any value found as a solution to the rational equation that is **also** an NPV is not an accepted solution. If this were the only solution, then it is stated that "no solutions exist."

From the initial rational equation in Example 2, the NPVs are $x \neq 0, 1$.

The derived solution of $x = 7$ is not among the NPVs, so it is an acceptable solution.

Step 6

Verify solutions.

Replace the solution value for the variable into the original rational equation and determine whether or not the equality is true. If not, there must have been an error somewhere along the way.

This step is not required unless stated, but it is recommended.

NOTES

Example 4

Solve the following expression.

$$3 + \frac{2}{3+x} = 5$$

Solution

$$\frac{3(3+x)}{1} + \frac{2(3+x)}{3+x} = \frac{5(3+x)}{1}$$

$$9 + 3x + 2 = 15 + 5x$$

$$11 + 3x = 15 + 5x$$

$$11 - 15 = 5x - 3x$$

$$-4 = 2x$$

$$x = -2$$

$$x \neq -3$$

The solution of $x = -2$ is not a non-permissible value, so this is the only valid solution.

Verification involves checking the left-hand side of the equation against the right-hand side.

LHS	RHS
$3 + \dfrac{2}{(3 + (-2))}$	5
$3 + \dfrac{2}{1}$	5
5	5

Since the left-hand side is equal to the right-hand side, the solution of -2 is verified.

PROBLEM SOLVING

Rational expressions and equations are frequently used to solve mathematical problems encountered in physics, engineering, mathematics, and everyday life.

To set up an appropriate equation, it is necessary to identify the variable(s) involved and translate a written (or spoken) problem into its mathematical equivalent. Once the rational equation is defined, the steps outlined in this chapter allow for solution and simplification.

Example 5

Write out and solve a rational equation for the problem below.

Stephen received a mark of 10 out of 25 on the first unit exam. The second unit exam is equally weighted and has the same number of questions. What mark does Stephen need to achieve on the second exam to receive an overall average of 50%?

A variable, such as x, represents an unknown quantity. Read questions carefully to see what quantity needs to be found. Often, the required quantity is stated at the end of the word problem.

Solution

To solve this problem, let x be the mark on the second exam. An average of the two exams will be produced by adding the two marks together and dividing by two. The desired mark is 50%. Set up as follows:

$$\frac{\left(\frac{10}{25}\right) + \left(\frac{x}{25}\right)}{2} = 50\%$$

$$\frac{\frac{10+x}{25}}{2} = 0.50$$

$$\frac{10+x}{25} = 1.00$$

$$10 + x = 25.00$$

$$x = 15.00$$

If Stephen achieves a mark of 15 out of 25, he will achieve an overall average of 50%.

Many word problems involve the relationship between distance, speed, and time. For these problems, the formulas required are

$$d = s \times t \qquad s = \frac{d}{t} \qquad t = \frac{d}{s}$$

d, s, t represent distance, speed, and time, respectively.

Example 6

Two cyclists are racing through the Rocky Mountains. Racer 2 is twice as fast as Racer 1. The route they take is 100 km long, and Racer 2 arrives at the finish line 2 h earlier than Racer 1. What is the speed of Racer 1?

Solution

Set up a rational equation using the variable x for the speed of Racer 1, and compare the two racers. The time for each cyclist to complete the route is found by the distance divided by their speeds.

Subtracting the faster cyclist's time from the slower cyclist's time will equal the difference in their arrival time (2 h).

$$\frac{100}{x} - \frac{100}{2x} = 2$$
$$\frac{100(2x)}{x} - \frac{100(2x)}{2x} = 2(2x)$$
$$200 - 100 = 4x$$
$$x = 25$$

The speed of Racer 1 is 25 km/h.

Other word problems involve the dimensions of three-dimensional objects and their area or volume. The formulas for these geometric problems are not included here and will generally be supplied in the question.

PRACTICE EXERCISES

1. Solve the rational equation below. State any restrictions on the variable.

$$\frac{2}{x-1} = \frac{3}{x}$$

2. Solve the following equation and state any NPVs.

$$\frac{3x+1}{6x} = \frac{x+1}{2x+1}$$

3. Solve the following equation. Hint: Try to solve by observation after the initial simplification.

$$\frac{x}{x+1} = \frac{-2}{2x+2}$$

4. For the rational equation below, state the LCM, NPVs, and then solve.

$$\frac{2}{x} - \frac{5}{3x} = 4$$

5. What is the solution to $\dfrac{13}{y+1} = 4$?

   A. $y = \dfrac{3}{2}$

   B. $y = \dfrac{9}{4}$

   C. $y = \dfrac{4}{9}$

   D. $y = \dfrac{2}{3}$

6. One winter day, a child makes two perfect cubes out of snow. The child made each side of the second cube twice as long as the first. The child's parent, a math teacher, comes out and cuts each cube exactly in half and puts one half from the small cube together with one half from the big cube. The parent determines that the total volume formed by adding one half of each size cube is $36\,\text{cm}^3$. What were the original dimensions of the small cube? A cube has three equal dimensions: length, width, and height. Its volume is determined by multiplying each of these three together.

REVIEW SUMMARY

In this unit, you have learned how to . . .

- reduce single-variable rational expressions containing monomials, binomials, and trinomials into their simplest equivalent form

- determine non-permissible values for single-variable rational expressions containing monomials, binomials, and trinomials

- multiply single-variable rational expressions

- divide single-variable rational expressions

- add single-variable rational expressions

- subtract single-variable rational expressions

- find and verify solutions to rational equations

- solve word problems involving rational equations

PRACTICE TEST

1. Which of the following expressions is an equivalent form of $\dfrac{2}{(x-1)}$?

   A. $\dfrac{2x^2}{x^2-1}$

   B. $\dfrac{3}{6(x-1)}$

   C. $\dfrac{2(x^2-1)}{(x+1)}$

   D. $\dfrac{4}{2x-2}$

2. Simplify the following expression by finding any common factors and cancelling. State any non-permissible values for the variable.

   $$\dfrac{2x^2-x-1}{(6x+3)}$$

3. A student wishes to create a rational expression with two non-permissible values. The NPVs are $a \neq 0, 1$. Which of the following statements is true?

   A. The expression must have the variable x in the numerator and the factors $(a)(a-1)$ in the denominator.

   B. The expression can have any number of factors involving the variable a in the numerator and denominator as long as after cancelling common factors, the denominator only contains the simplified factors of $(a)(a-1)$.

   C. One possible expression that the student could use $\dfrac{1}{(x)(x-1)}$.

   D. One possible expression that the student could use it is $\dfrac{2}{2a^2-2a}$.

4. Rectangle A has an area that is represented by the expression $x^2 + 4x - 5$ and a width of $x - 1$. Rectangle B has an area represented by the expression $x^2 - 4$ and a width of $x - 2$. Write an expression, in simplified form, for the length of Rectangle A divided by the length of Rectangle B. List any non-permissible values.

5. When the following division of rational expressions is simplified, the numerator is 1. Given this fact, solve for the unknown constant a. State all non-permissible values.

$$\frac{(x+2)(x-3)}{(x-a)^2} \div \frac{x^2 - x - 6}{x - 1}$$

6. Perform the indicated addition and subtraction and simplify the following expression. State all NPVs.

$$\frac{9}{x} + \frac{4}{3} - \frac{9}{4}$$

7. Solve and verify your answer for the following problem:

Half of an unknown number is added to one quarter of the original unknown number, and the result is equal to ten. What is the unknown number?

8. Molly must obtain an average mark of 50% to pass her math course. There are six equally weighted tests in the course, and Molly received 50% on four of the tests and 52% on one of the tests. What is the minimum mark that she must achieve on her sixth test in order to pass the course?

9. It is Christmas, and Grandpa wants to mail 10 individual cubic boxes in one large cubic box. Each individual box has side lengths of 5 cm. What is the minimum volume that the large box must have to fit all the small boxes?

Hint: Solve logically, rather than by an equation.

EXPONENTS AND RADICALS

When you are finished this unit, you should be able to . . .
- classify numbers according to the number sets
- use approximate representations of irrational numbers
- communicate a set of instructions used to solve an arithmetic problem
- perform arithmetic operations on irrational numbers by using appropriate decimal approximations
- use exponent laws for powers with rational exponents
- simplify radicals
- add, subtract, multiply, and divide radicals as exact values

PREREQUISITE SKILLS AND KNOWLEDGE

Prior to beginning this unit, you should be able to . . .

- apply exponent laws to powers with numbers for bases
- apply the order of operations
- use the distributive property on polynomials
- reduce fractions
- recognize perfect squares

Lesson 1 NUMBER SETS

In the study of mathematics, it is not always enough to say that a number is just a number. Mathematicians have placed all numbers in categories, from the everyday counting numbers 1, 2, 3, ... etc., to complex numbers that have no end to their decimals, such as π (pi).

All the number sets listed below are included within the real number system. Each number set has its own symbol (or symbols) as well as restrictions on membership in its elite club. As in real life, it is possible for a member of one club to be a member of another as well. Indeed, entire sets are "nested" within other sets. Keep this in mind as the number sets are introduced.

Natural Numbers (N)

The natural numbers are often called the "counting numbers."

The set includes: $\{1, 2, 3, 4, ...\}$

Whole Numbers (W)

These include all the counting numbers as well as zero. The natural numbers set is "nested" within the set of whole numbers. If the natural numbers set is represented as being contained within a circle, a larger circle surrounding it would represent the whole numbers.

The set includes: $\{0, 1, 2, 3, 4, ...\}$

Integers (Z or I)

Although uppercase I is often used to denote integers, the correct symbol is an uppercase Z, which is derived from the German word *zahlen* meaning "to count." The integers include all the counting numbers, their additive inverses (negative counterparts), and zero. Note that by this definition, the set of natural numbers and the slightly larger set of whole numbers are both nested within the set of integers.

The set includes: $\{... -4, -3, -2, -1, 0, 1, 2, 3, 4, ...\}$

Rational Numbers (Q)

The symbol Q is from the German word for *quotient*, which can be defined as a ratio. Any number that can be expressed by the quotient $\left(\dfrac{a}{b}\right)$, where both a and b are integers and b is not zero, is a rational number. The restriction on b is to avoid division by zero, which is undefined.

Consider that the number 6 can be expressed as $\dfrac{6}{1}$, where the numerator and denominator are both integers. So, 6 is a rational number. It is also a natural number, a whole number, and an integer.

DECIMAL RATIONALS

Up to this point, it is relatively easy to place a given number into a set that it belongs to or even to list all the sets that it belongs to. Rational numbers include a whole set of decimal numbers that do not belong to any previously listed set. Recall that if there is a quotient $\frac{a}{b}$, where a and b are integers and $b \neq 0$, the result is a rational number. Decimals can easily result from this quotient.

Example 1

Divide 1 by 8 and find the decimal result.

Solution

$$\frac{1}{8} = 0.125$$

This is a terminating decimal. Its value can be completely defined by a finite set of digits.

There are decimals that do not terminate, but do repeat. Consider the following example.

Example 2

Without using technology, convert the repeating decimal 0.333 3… into a fraction, if possible. Is this a rational number?

Solution

Let $a = 0.333\,3\ldots$
This repeats after one decimal place, so multiply it by 10^1.
$10a = 3.333\,3\ldots$

Subtract the a from the $10a$, obtaining $9a = 3$, or just $a = \frac{1}{3}$.
By this method, the repeating decimal 0.333 3… has been converted to a quotient of integers $\left(\frac{1}{3}\right)$. So, the repeating decimal is indeed a rational number.

Fractions and decimal values between whole number values are not included in the natural, whole, or integer number systems.

(e.g., $\frac{1}{4}$ and 2.5 are not included.)

Terminating means "ending." A terminating number is one that ends. (e.g., 4.769)

When the denominator of a particular fraction is a 7, and the fraction does not reduce to an integer, the corresponding decimal number is a six-digit non-terminating number with a set pattern.

$\frac{6}{7}$ is an example of a number which does not terminate, but does repeat.

Example 3

A student wishes to see if any repeating decimal is a rational number, so the student makes up the following: 0.121 2….
What fraction has the student created?

Solution

Let $a = 0.121\ 2\ldots$

This repeats after two decimal places, so multiply by 10^2.

$100a = 12.121\ 2\ldots$

Subtract to obtain $99a = 12$ or $a = \dfrac{12}{99}$, which reduces to $\dfrac{4}{33}$.

Although this was a randomly created repeating decimal (and so not deductive proof), the student has correctly surmised that any repeating decimal is a rational number.

Irrational Numbers ($\overline{Q}$)

Any decimal numbers that does not terminate AND does not repeat is an irrational number.

Whereas the rational numbers have every other previously described number set nested within this set, the irrational numbers have only their own members.

Real Numbers ($\mathbb{R}$)

The double-stroke uppercase $\mathbb{R}$ is the symbol for this set, which includes all rational and irrational numbers.

There is one more set of numbers that you may encounter in higher mathematics known as the unreal, or imaginary numbers.

CONVERTING DECIMALS TO FRACTIONS

Technology readily allows for the conversion of decimals to fractions, however, knowing the algebraic method is further enrichment. Examples 2 and 3 above described the conversion of repeating decimals to fractions. More decimals are examined here.

Example 4

Convert 0.25 to a fraction.

Solution

You may or may not recognize this as the decimal form of $\dfrac{1}{4}$.

To show the solution algebraically, multiply the decimal by whatever power of 10 is necessary to bring all numbers to the left of the decimal point.

Let $a = 0.25$. Then $100a = 25$. Now, divide to find a (as a fraction).

$$a = \frac{25}{100} \qquad \text{Now, reduce to simplest form.}$$

$$a = \frac{1}{4}$$

This method is slightly different from the method described for repeating decimals. If the decimal has a non-repeating amount before the repeating decimal, deal with it as follows.

Example 5

Convert 1.235 35…. to a fraction.

Solution

Consider this as $1 + 0.2 + 0.035\,35\ldots$

Treat each term separately, finding its fractional equivalent, then add at the end.

The first term, 1, has a fractional equivalent of $\frac{1}{1}$.

Let $a = 0.2$. Then, $10a = 2$, so $a = \frac{2}{10}$, or $a = \frac{1}{5}$.

Let $b = 0.035\,35\ldots$
$100\,b = 3.535\,35\ldots$

So, $99b = 3.5$ (now multiply by 10 again)
$990b = 35$
$$b = \frac{35}{990} \text{ or } \frac{7}{198}$$

The final fraction is

$$\frac{1}{1} + \frac{1}{5} + \frac{7}{198} \quad \text{LCD is } (5)(198)$$

$$\frac{990}{990} + \frac{198}{990} + \frac{35}{990}$$

$$\frac{1\,223}{990}$$

Decimal questions of this difficulty are rare at this level.

NOTES

SQUARE (OR CUBIC) ROOTS AS DECIMALS

At this point, it is possible to take any given number and place it within one or more number sets where it belongs. The key to determining if a decimal number is rational or irrational, rests in determining whether the decimal terminates or repeats, or does neither. However, what if the number given is in the form $\sqrt{3}$?

It is not correct to simply look at the 3 and say that this is an integer (also a natural, whole, and rational number).

The square root operation must be applied first, before any determination can be made regarding the number set.

$$\sqrt{3} = 1.732\,050\,80 \ldots$$

This decimal neither repeats nor terminates. So, the square root of 3 represents an irrational number.

$$\sqrt[3]{8} = 2$$

So, the cubed root of 8 is a rational number.

Note that radicals will be dealt with in-depth in the following lessons.

For now, you will simply use technology to convert squares and higher roots to decimals. Then, your knowledge of the number sets will apply.

PRACTICE EXERCISES

1. Match the numbers on the left with the number systems on the right. Note that each number and system can only be used once (even though some numbers belong to more than one set).

    4   *Natural*

    $\sqrt{3}$ *Whole*

    1.44   *Integer*

    0   *Rational*

    −3   *Irrational*

2. Joe wishes to explain that the number 6 is actually a rational number. To do this, he could

    A. express 6 as $\dfrac{18}{2}$

    B. express 6 as $\dfrac{6}{1}$

    C. explain that since 6 is a natural number, whole number, and integer, it must be rational, as all rational numbers are one of these

    D. explain that 6 is an imaginary number

3. A student is given a number with 4 decimal places, represented by the unknown $0.xyx\,y$. Is this a rational or irrational number?

4. How many number sets are "nested" within the set of integers (not counting the set of integers itself)? Name one. How many number sets are "nested" within the set of irrational numbers (not counting the set of irrationals itself)?

5. What is the name and symbol for the set of numbers that includes all rational and irrational numbers?

6. Convert 0.4 and 0.666… to their respective fractional forms.

Lesson 2 CALCULATIONS WITH REAL NUMBERS

Calculators and other technology are used to find the square root or cube root just as they are used to find a number squared or cubed. Most students at this level can use their calculator to find not only the square root, but actually any n^{th} root, just as they can find a number squared, or raised to any power of n.

However, it is beneficial to be able to understand the approximate value of a number, whether that number is represented by a fraction or a root.

Example 1

Complete the following chart using a calculator for assistance if necessary.

$\sqrt{100} =$

$\sqrt{81} =$

$\sqrt{64} =$

$\sqrt{49} =$

$\sqrt{36} =$

$\sqrt{25} =$

$\sqrt{16} =$

$\sqrt{9} =$

$\sqrt{4} =$

$\sqrt{1} =$

Solution

$\sqrt{100} = 10$

$\sqrt{81} = 9$

$\sqrt{64} = 8$

$\sqrt{49} = 7$

$\sqrt{36} = 6$

$\sqrt{25} = 5$

$\sqrt{16} = 4$

$\sqrt{9} = 3$

$\sqrt{4} = 2$

$\sqrt{1} = 1$

Knowing the values of the square root for at least the numbers up to 100 that generate integers is a key tool for estimating.

Example 2

A student wishes to find $\sqrt{40}$ by estimation with no calculator. What would be the best guess (as an integer)?

Solution

If the student memorized the chart above, or just knew the square roots, he or she would be able to ascertain that $\sqrt{36} = 6$ and that $\sqrt{49} = 7$. Since $\sqrt{40}$ is closer to $\sqrt{36}$ than $\sqrt{49}$ (just by comparing the numbers), the answer should be closer to 6 than 7. In actuality, the value of $\sqrt{40}$ is approximately 6.32. The best guess is 6.

ROUNDING NUMBERS

Also known as rounding off, this skill is briefly reviewed here, as the basics should already be known.

4.56 is given as a decimal. The question asks for the answer to be rounded to the nearest tenth (or first decimal place). This leaves 4.5_ where the blank, _, is to be considered. If the number in the blank is 5 or greater, round the 4.5 to 4.6. If the number in the blank is less than 5, it is not considered, and the rounded answer 4.5.

Only the next number is considered in rounding, where "next" is one decimal place past the requested rounding.

Approximations vary greatly depending on whether a calculator is allowed or not.
The approximate value of $\sqrt{5}$, using no calculator is the integer 2. The approximate value of $\sqrt{5}$, using a calculator, involves rounding off to two decimal places and obtaining 2.24 instead of 2.236 06….

For an approximation of $2\sqrt{5}$, it is expected that you input 2 times the square root of 5 into your calculator. Find the answer and round appropriately. Without the calculator, this would be an approximation of 2 times 2, or 4.

Example 3

Round $\dfrac{1}{8}$ to the nearest hundredth.

Solution

First, the fraction must be put into decimal form: 0.125. The nearest hundredth means round to two decimal places. The next number after 2, is 5, so round the 2 up to give 0.13 as the answer. If the fraction had have been 0.124, then rounding to the nearest hundredth would have produced 0.12 as the answer.

CUBE ROOTS

The list of cube roots that are expected to be known is much smaller than the list of square roots presented earlier. Consider the numbers from 1 to 5 cubed. Then, express the cube roots of those larger numbers.

$1^3 = 1$ $\sqrt[3]{1} = 1$

$2^3 = 8$ $\sqrt[3]{8} = 2$

$3^3 = 27$ $\sqrt[3]{27} = 3$

$4^3 = 64$ $\sqrt[3]{64} = 4$

$5^3 = 125$ $\sqrt[3]{125} = 5$

The process of cubing a number, or finding the cube root, changes the number more dramatically than squaring or the square root.

Example 4

Estimate, without a calculator, the value of $\sqrt[3]{24}$.

Solution

Knowing that $\sqrt[3]{8} = 2$ and $\sqrt[3]{27} = 3$, $\sqrt[3]{24}$ will be much closer to 3 than to 2. A correct estimate would be 3.

Using a calculator and rounding to the nearest tenth, the answer is 2.9 (rounded from 2.88…).

NUMBER LINES AND IRRATIONAL NUMBERS

The idea of a number line is not new, however, the ability to place newly learned irrational numbers in their proper place on a number line is a new skill. For instance, where would $\sqrt{3}$ be on a number line? Between 1 and 2 or 2 and 3? The best method for finding the solution is to find the decimal value (approximation or not) and use that as a determination.

But, just as you should not need to use technology to evaluate $\sqrt{4}$ very much longer, you should come to the point where you know, without needing a calculator, that $\sqrt{3}$ is larger than 1.

NOTES

Example 5

Evaluate the following numbers, and place them in their proper place (approximate scale) on the line given. Which of the numbers are irrational?

$$\frac{1}{4}, \sqrt[3]{8}, \sqrt{2}, \sqrt{3}, \sqrt{5}, 2\sqrt{2}, \frac{14}{5}$$

0 ---------- 1 ---------- 2 ---------- 3

Solution

First, find the decimal values for the given numbers.
Then, place them along the line in the appropriate spots.
List the irrational numbers.

The numbers listed above, converted to decimals, are:
0.25, 2, 1.414…, 1.732…, 2.236…, 2.828…, 2.8.

Placed along the line:

$$0 -- \left(\frac{1}{4}\right) -- 1 -- \left(\sqrt{2}\right) -- \left(\sqrt{3}\right) -- 2 -- \left(\sqrt{5}\right) -- \left(\frac{14}{5}\right) -- 3 --$$
$$\left(\sqrt[3]{8}\right)$$

Since the cubed root of 8 is equal to 2, it had to be placed below the line for clarity.

The irrational numbers are the $\sqrt{2}, \sqrt{3}, \sqrt{5},$ and $\sqrt[2]{2}$.

Knowing the values and approximations of a number of key irrationals, and aided by a calculator when necessary, it is possible to assess the accuracy of statements or estimates.

Example 6

A student not quite certain about the value of irrational numbers thinks that $\sqrt{4} + \sqrt{9} + \sqrt{25} = \sqrt{38}$, since all the numbers seem to add up under the root sign. Using known values or estimates, consider the accuracy of this assumption.

Solution

The first three square roots should be known to be 2 + 3 + 5, or 10 in total. The value of $\sqrt{38}$ must lie between the values of $\sqrt{36}$ and $\sqrt{49}$. That is, between 6 and 7. So, this assumption is incorrect.

ABSOLUTE VALUE AND ORDER OF OPERATIONS (REVIEW)

Absolute value is also involved in coordinate geometry as the distance between two points, one of which may be below the zero axis.

The absolute value of a real number is the distance along a number line that the number is from zero. The number -5 is 5 units away from zero in the negative direction. The number $+5$ is 5 units from zero in the positive direction. The absolute value of a negative number is equal to its positive counterpart.

Absolute value is indicated by straight brackets $|\ \ |$ with the value to be determined placed between them.

$$|-5| = 5$$
$$|-8| + |2| - |-4| = (8) + (2) - (4) = 6$$

The various mathematical operations, such as multiplication, addition, etc., are performed in a particular sequence based on order of priority. This is also called the Order of Operations. The mnemonic device PEDMAS is sometimes used to aid the memorization of this order.

P: Parenthesis (or brackets). Parenthesis must be cleared first, if possible. Note that $(x+1)^2$ suggests we must add x and 1 first, before applying the exponential, but if the variable is unknown, we cannot do it. Proceed to next step. If there are multiple brackets, solve the inner $(\ )$ before the middle $\{\ \}$, and then the last $[\ ]$.

E: Exponent (or roots). Solve any roots or exponents next.

D: Division. And the next step, multiplication are equal/opposite procedures so these two steps are interchangeable.
$$(A)(B) = (A) \div \frac{1}{(B)}.$$

M: Multiplication. See division above.

A: Addition. Next, add and subtract from left to right.

S: Subtraction

Throughout this course, questions and examples may arise where the order of operations must be applied.

You may choose to immediately convert the diameter to a radius by dividing it in half. Then, simply use the radius in the calculations. If you do not do this, then the keystrokes needed to enter the formula properly are different. With most math questions, it is not always necessary to enter every value into the calculator, as shown, if some mental math can be applied along the way.

Here, the radius is going to be squared because of the formula. It is determined that the radius is $\sqrt{2}$. If you have already deduced that the square of $\sqrt{2}$ is just 2, there is no need for you to input a square root value squared.

PROBLEM SOLVING

Using the skills learned up to this point, it is possible to present and solve a number of problems with the assistance of technology, when applicable.

Example 7

A student is told that the area of a circle can be found by the formula $A = \pi r^2$. It is known that the diameter of the circle in question is $2\sqrt{2}$ units. What steps must be taken to solve this question, and what is the answer rounded to the nearest hundredth?

Solution

The area is found by multiplying pi (π) by the radius squared.

The radius is half the diameter, so $\dfrac{2\sqrt{2}}{2} = r = \sqrt{2}$. The radius

squared is $\left(\sqrt{2}\right)^2 = 2$. The deductive proof of this has not yet been investigated, but you may have determined this already intuitively. By using the π button on the calculator, it can be determined that the answer is 6.283 1…, so the area is approximately 6.28 units squared.

Example 8

A student is solving a problem involving a right-angled triangle with the two smaller sides of length $\sqrt{17}$ and $\sqrt{24}$. The student knows the Pythagorean theorem, which states $c^2 = a^2 + b^2$, where c is the length of the longest side of a right triangle, and a and b are the other sides. Use approximations to find the final side (using a calculator only for squaring, not square root) and then use the formula (with the aid of a calculator throughout) to find the actual value (round at the end to the nearest hundredth).

Solution

By approximation: approximate the lengths as 4 and 5 (since $\sqrt{17}$ is just a little more than $\sqrt{16}$, and $\sqrt{24}$ is just a little less than $\sqrt{25}$). Use the calculator to square these and add them, to get the answer 41. Now, approximate $\sqrt{41}$ as somewhere between 6 and 7. The question did not ask for an integer approximation, so 6.4 should be a good approximation.

By calculator: $\sqrt{17}$ is calculated, and then squared to arrive at 17. The other side is squared to return to 24. $c^2 = 41$, $c = 6.403\ 12....$

Rounding this to the nearest hundredth gives 6.40, which is the same as the above approximation. It turns out the approximation was so close because the radicals expressing the lengths of the sides were very close to the exact value squares. Not all approximations are this accurate.

PRACTICE EXERCISES

1. Using a calculator, find the value of $\sqrt{16}$. Now, find $\sqrt{\sqrt{16}}$ by taking the square root of the answer found initially. Then, try calculating $\sqrt{\sqrt{16}}$ in one step on your calculator. Is the answer different?

2. Follow the steps provided, performing each operation individually. First, choose any natural number and then add 3 to that number. Now, multiply the total by 4 and then subtract 8. Divide your total by 4. Subtract your original number. What answer do you arrive at? Try again with any other number (a negative integer, zero, etc). Do the results change? Write these steps as an algebraic equation.

3. Round the following numbers to three decimal places. Add them and then round them to the nearest hundredth. Now, express the same numbers as decimals to two decimal places (by rounding) and then add them. Compare the answers.

$$\sqrt{2} \qquad \sqrt{3} \qquad \frac{2}{7}$$

4. From a fixed starting point called ground zero, two soldiers walk in opposite directions. Soldier A indicates his position as –8 m after 1 minute. Soldier B, after the same 1 minute, indicates his position as +9 m. To find their distance from each other, one should

   A. use the absolute values of their positions and add
   B. simply add their two reported positions
   C. approximate their distance as double one soldier's distance
   D. repeat the experiment using the 90° rotation distance

5. Place the following three numbers in order from smallest to largest:

$$\left|-32\right| \qquad\qquad (-3)^2 \qquad\qquad \sqrt[3]{1\,000}$$

6. A student is given the problem $3-(2+3)^2-4\div2$ and asked to use the correct order of operations to solve it.
operations to solve it.
What is the correct answer?

Lesson 3 RADICALS AND EXPONENTS

Up to this point, $\sqrt{2}$ has been simply called root two, or the square root of two. This is now defined as a radical. As well, $\sqrt[3]{8}$, the cube root of eight, is also a radical. Consider the following terms and ideas.

$\sqrt[2]{16}$

Here, the number 16 is called the radicand. The small number, 2, is called the index. The sign so far known as the root sign is actually called the radical sign. Any number or value that contains the radical sign is called a radical.

$\sqrt[n]{x}$

Here, the unknown variable x is the radicand, the unknown variable n is the index, and the familiar radical sign is present.

Note that the index is not always shown. In square roots, which are the most common, the index of two is simply understood. It can be written, but does not have to be. This is similar to saying x instead of $1x$.

LAWS OF EXPONENTS

To investigate radicals and their properties, it is essential to review and understand the laws governing exponents. Many of these laws will be familiar, through example or use, though not as a set rule as of yet.

Example 1

How can $(2)(2)(2)$ be expressed as a single number raised to an exponent?

Solution

Two times two times two is the same as 2^3, or two cubed, which is equal to 8.

2^3 is two cubed, but more technically it is the base 2 raised to the exponent 3.

In the example above, a number was raised to an exponent (a power).
It is possible that the number is unknown, or a variable.
The general laws governing exponents are written with variables so that they can be applied to any given number. The laws and some examples follow. In each case, the general form of the law is given, then applied to an example using numbers to illustrate.

| |

a) $x^n \cdot x^m = x^{n+m}$ or $2^2 \cdot 2^3 = 2^5$

$(2)(2) \cdot (2)(2)(2) = 2^5$

b) $\dfrac{x^n}{x^m} = x^{n-m}$ or $\dfrac{x^5}{x^2} = x^3$

$\dfrac{(x)(x)(x)(x)(x)}{(x)(x)} = \dfrac{(x)(x)(x)}{1}$

Example 2

Using the second law shown above, show the expected result of $2^3 \div 2^7$. Then, show the result of $\dfrac{2^3}{2^7}$ by expansion and cancelling like terms. Compare the results.

Solution

For division where the bases (2) are the same, the exponents are subtracted.

$2^3 \div 2^7 = 2^{3-7} = 2^{-4}$.

By expansion, $\dfrac{(2)(2)(2)}{(2)(2)(2)(2)(2)(2)(2)} = \dfrac{1}{(2)(2)(2)(2)}$.

Each of the factors of (2) in the numerator cancels one factor of (2) in the denominator, leaving the given result. $\dfrac{1}{2^4}$.

By the example, it is shown that $x^{-n} = \dfrac{1}{x^n}$.

What happens when the case is $x^n \div x^n$? This is $\dfrac{x^n}{x^n} = x^{n-n} = x^0$.

Any number divided by itself is equal to 1 (except division by zero).

So, $x^0 = 1$.

c) $x^{-n} = \dfrac{1}{x^n}$ or $x^{-1} = \dfrac{1}{x}$ or $3^{-2} = \dfrac{1}{3^2} = \dfrac{1}{9}$

d) $x^0 = 1$ or $124^0 = 1$ or $\dfrac{124^1}{124^1} = \dfrac{1}{1} = 124^{1-1}$

Additional laws include:

e) $(x^n)^m = x^{nm}$ or

$$(4)^2 = 16$$
$$(2^2)^2 = 2^4 = 16$$

f) $(xy)^n = x^n y^n$ or

$$(2x)^2 = 4x^2$$
$$(2x)^2 = 2^2(x)^2 = 4x^2$$

g) $\left(\dfrac{x}{y}\right)^n = \dfrac{x^n}{y^n}$ or

$$\left(\frac{4}{2}\right)^2 = \frac{4^2}{2^2} = \frac{16}{4} = 4$$
$$\left(\frac{4}{2}\right)^2 = (2)^2 = 4$$

h) $\left(\dfrac{x}{y}\right)^{-n} = \left(\dfrac{y}{x}\right)^n$

This is an extension of law c. The negative exponent is forcing each base to the other side of the fraction (division) and changing the exponent into a positive exponent. If the base begins in the denominator with a negative exponent, it moves to the numerator and becomes positive.

Applying these laws allows for problems to be solved that involve not only exponents, but also unknown variables (as well as known numbers).

Example 3

Simplify the expression $\dfrac{24x^2 y}{(2)^3 xy}$.

Solution

This question can be worked out two ways, as shown below.

$$\frac{(3)(8)(x)(x)(y)}{(8)(x)(y)}$$

$$\frac{(3)(x)}{1}$$

$$3x$$

$$\left(\frac{24}{8}\right)\left(x^{2-1}\right)\left(y^{1-1}\right)$$

$$(3)\left(x^1\right)\left(y^0\right)$$

$$3x(1)$$

$$3x$$

The first method involves breaking the terms up into factors and then cancelling like terms to produce the simplest result.

The second method involves determining the numerical quotient and multiplying this by the variable quotient. The variables are dealt with using the laws of exponents regarding division. Both answers produce the same result.

RADICALS AS EXPONENTIALS

Now that a full set of laws regarding exponents is in place, these laws could be applied to radicals if the radicals were able to be rewritten as exponentials.

Can $\sqrt{2}$ be written as a base and an exponent? Consider that $\left(\sqrt{2}\right)^2 = 2$. This is known from a previous exercise, but you can confirm this by using a calculator.

Let us express $\sqrt{2}$ as 2^x (the base two raised to an unknown power).

Then, given $\left(\sqrt{2}\right)\left(\sqrt{2}\right) = 2$, it must be true that $(2)^x (2)^x = 2^1$.

By the law of exponents, the two exponents, x, must add together to equal 1. $x + x = 1, 2x = 1, x = \dfrac{1}{2}$.

Examples can be tested, using different bases and applying the laws of exponents to prove the case for $\sqrt[3]{8}$ and other known values. Additional verifications are not presented here.

Therefore, $\sqrt{2} = 2^{\frac{1}{2}}$.

Radicals can be expressed as a base and an exponent given the following:

$\sqrt[3]{8}$

The number inside the radical sign (radicand) becomes the base. This base is already being raised to the power of 1 (exponent 1) even though it is not shown. The index becomes the new denominator for the exponent.
So, instead of 8 being raised to an exponent of 1 it can be rewritten, outside of the radical sign, with an exponent of $\dfrac{1}{3}$.

$\sqrt[3]{8} = 8^{\frac{1}{3}}$

Here, the radical form has been rewritten in exponential form. Now, all the laws of exponents can be applied.

Example 4

Give simple proof that shows that $\sqrt[3]{8}$ is the same as $8^{\frac{1}{3}}$, by expanding the 8 into its factors of 2.

Solution

It has already been shown and can be confirmed by a calculator that the cube root of 8 is equal to 2. $\sqrt[3]{8} = 2$. It is suggested that this is also equal to $8^{\frac{1}{3}}$. Is $8^{\frac{1}{3}} = 2$?

$8^{\frac{1}{3}} = (8)^{\frac{1}{3}} = (2 \times 2 \times 2)^{\frac{1}{3}} = \left(2^3\right)^{\frac{1}{3}}$ and, by the law of exponents,

$\left(2^3\right)^{\frac{1}{3}} = 2^{\frac{3}{1} \cdot \frac{1}{3}} = 2^{\frac{3}{3}} = 2$

GENERAL EXPONENTIAL FORM FOR RADICALS

A radical given in the form $\sqrt[n]{x}$ can be rewritten as $x^{\frac{1}{n}}$. If the radical appears more complicated, such as $\sqrt[n]{x^m}$, this is rewritten as $x^{\frac{m}{n}}$.

Exponents share some similar qualities with multiplication and division.

If a number is given, and then that number is going to be multiplied by 4 and divided by 2, it does not matter what step is done first.

$4 \cdot 4 \div 2$ with the multiplication first, 16 is divided by 2, which equals 8.

$4 \cdot 4 \div 2$ with the division first, 4 is multiplied by 2, which equals 8.

In the same manner, for a number that is going to be squared, then the square root taken, the order does not matter.

$4^2 = 16$

$\sqrt{16} = 4$

$\sqrt{4} = 2$

$2^2 = 4$

Because of this property, it is possible to write:

$x^{\frac{m}{n}} = \sqrt[n]{x^m} = \left(\sqrt[n]{x}\right)^m$

At this point, it is not necessary to cover the idea that n^{th} roots exist for negative numbers only if n is odd, and that it is possible to have a positive and negative answer for a square root derived from an equation.

Given $x^2 = 4$, two possibilities exist for x. However, when the square root is already expressed in the form $x = \sqrt{4}$, only the positive is required.

PERFECT SQUARES AND CUBES

Recall and review the values of x^2 and x^3 for the first several integer values of x.

$$1^2 = 1 \qquad 1^3 = 1$$

$$2^2 = 4 \qquad 2^3 = 8$$

$$3^2 = 9 \qquad 3^3 = 27$$

...   ...

This knowledge will be essential to rewrite radicals into exponential form. For instance, whenever 8 appears as the radicand of a cube root, this can be switched with 2^3. The cube root of a number cubed simply produces the number. Consider the following examples.

Example 5

Express $25^{\frac{3}{2}}$ in radical form and as a number raised to the exponent 1
(i.e., no exponent needs to be written).

Solution

By definition, $25^{\frac{3}{2}} = \sqrt[2]{25^3} = \left(\sqrt{25}\right)^3$.

Knowing that it does not matter whether the number 25 is cubed and then the square root taken, or the other way around, it is possible to find the answer without the assistance of a calculator.

Since 25 has a perfect square root of 5, the square root is performed first. Now, 5 is raised to the exponent 3, which is 5 times 5 times 5. The answer is 125. If 25 were first cubed, then the square root of this number taken, a calculator would have been needed.

$$\sqrt[2]{25^3} = 125$$

Changing a radical, or a number with a rational exponent, into a number with an exponent of 1, is often called evaluating, or simplifying.

Example 6

Evaluate $(-8)^{\frac{-2}{3}}$.

Solution

This can be rewritten as a radical, but that is not required. The 3 in the denominator means the cube root. The cube root of –8 is –2. (Check by calculator, or consider that $(-2)^3 = -8$)

The problem has now been reduced to $(-2)^{-2}$. By the law of exponents, this can be rewritten as $\left(\dfrac{1}{-2}\right)^2$. Notice that the negative exponent has moved the base to the denominator from the numerator.
It has also moved the 1 from the denominator to the numerator.
The exponent is now positive. However, the number (base) itself does not lose its negative value. A common mistake is to remove **all** negatives by switching the numerator and denominator.

$$\left(-\frac{1}{2}\right)^2 = \frac{1}{4}$$

$$(-8)^{\frac{-2}{3}} = \frac{1}{4}$$

Knowing the first few perfect cubes and the first ten or so perfect squares, will greatly assist you in solving radical evaluations.

Some questions do not require a number to be evaluated. Often, a variable is given in exponential form and needs to be rewritten or simplified in some way. Sometimes, a series of variables are multiplied, divided, etc. Here, apply the laws of exponents throughout and the problem can be methodically solved. Remember to only add or subtract exponents from bases that are the same.

NOTES

Example 7

Simplify $(x)(x)^{\frac{2}{3}}(y)$.

Solution

Add the exponents on the variable x, and then rewrite with y unchanged.

$$x^{\frac{1}{1}}x^{\frac{2}{3}}y$$

$$x^{\frac{1}{1}+\frac{2}{3}}y$$

$$x^{\frac{3}{3}+\frac{2}{3}}y$$

$$x^{\frac{5}{3}}y$$

This may not appear simpler, but combining the two x variables into a single x, raised to the exponent given, is preferred.

PRACTICE EXERCISES

1. Rewrite $\sqrt[5]{13^3}$ in exponential form (a base raised to a rational exponent).

2. What is the index of $\sqrt{12^2}$? What would be the base if it were rewritten in exponential form? Evaluate the radicand (expand under the radical sign to obtain the actual radicand). What is the sum of the radicand and the index?

3. Clear the brackets and simplify the expression $\left(\dfrac{2}{x}\right)^3$ if possible.

4. Express $\left(\dfrac{3}{4}\right)^{-2}$ as a decimal, rounded to two decimal places.

5. Express all the numbers in the expression $\dfrac{2^3}{8}$ as powers of 2 and evaluate.

6. Express $(x)^{\frac{2}{3}}(x)^{\frac{2}{3}}(x)^{\frac{2}{3}}$ as a single x raised to a rational exponent.

Lesson 4 USING EXPONENT LAWS TO SIMPLIFY, EVALUATE, AND IDENTIFY PATTERNS

You can use the exponent laws learned in the previous lessons to simplify, evaluate, and identify patterns. The exponent laws reduce the number of calculations needed to solve problems and assist in identifying patterns in problems.

For example, to find the product $3^3 \times 3^5$ without using exponent laws, you would expand and multiply.

$$3^3 \times 3^5 = 3 \times 3 \times 3 \times 3 \times 3 \times 3 \times 3 \times 3 = 6\,561$$

However, using the exponent laws, you can shorten the process.

$$3^3 \times 3^5 = 3^{3+5} = 3^8$$

Example 1

What is the next term in the sequence $2^3, 2^2, 2^1, 2^0, 2^{-1}, 2^{-2}, 2^{-3} \ldots$?

Solution

2^{-4}

Example 2

What is the relationship between 2^3 and 2^{-3}?

Solution

The value 2^{-3} is the reciprocal of 2^3.

$$2^{-3} = \frac{1}{2^3} = \frac{1}{8} \text{ and } 2^3 = 8$$

This relationship illustrates the negative exponent law, which states that a base to a negative exponent is the reciprocal of the base to a positive exponent.

Example 3

How are the expressions $(-2)^4$ and -2^4 different?

Solution

The expression $(-2)^4$ means $-2 \times -2 \times -2 \times -2 = 16$, while the expression -2^4 means $-2 \times 2 \times 2 \times 2 = -16$. Since the negative symbol is not contained within brackets, it represents a coefficient of (-1). Following the order of operations (BEDMAS), the power is always dealt with first and the coefficient is multiplied later.

NOTES

NOTES

Example 4

If the price of a hamburger doubles every two years, what will it cost in 50 years?

Solution

Start by identifying the pattern. Pick a starting price for the hamburger, for example, $1.

Year	Year 0	Year 2	Year 4	Year 6	Year 8
Price	$1	$2	$4	$8	$16

Since the price of the hamburger is doubling, the base number will be 2.

Since the price doubles every two years, take the total number years and divide by 2 to get the exponent.

Using $2^{\left(\frac{50}{2}\right)} \times$ the original value of the hamburger, you get

$2^{\left(\frac{50}{2}\right)} \times \$1 = \$33\ 554\ 432$.

So, the price of the hamburger in 50 years would be $33 554 432.

Example 5

Simplify the expression $n^{-2} \times n^5$ and then evaluate for $n = 2$.

Solution

$$n^{-2} \times n^5 = n^{-2+5}$$
$$= n^3$$
$$= (2)^3$$
$$= 8$$

Always put the value being substituted into the question in brackets.

194

Example 6

Use exponent laws to help you solve the following equations.

a) $n^4 \times n^2 = 64$

Solution

$n^6 = 64$

You can use a calculator and the "guess-and-test" method to find a number to the 6th power that gives an answer of 64. The correct solution is $n = 2$.

b) $n^{-5} = \dfrac{1}{32}$

Solution

$\dfrac{1}{n^5} = \dfrac{1}{32}$ is an equivalent form to the above equation.

Now use the "guess-and-test" method to find a number to the 5th power that equals 32. The solution is $n = 2$.

Example 7

When expanded, what are the last two digits of 11^{100}?

Solution

Use your calculator to find the last two digits for the first nine values with a base of 11.

Power	11^0	11^1	11^2	11^3	11^4	11^5	11^6	11^7	11^8	11^9
Last two digits	01	11	21	31	41	51	61	71	81	91

Notice that the tens digit matches the exponent in each case. When we get to 11^{10}, the pattern will repeat, giving 101. Thus, 10^{100} would go through the above pattern 10 times, and the last two digits of 11^{100} would be 01.

Since squaring and taking the square root are opposite operations, n^6 and $\sqrt[6]{n}$ are opposite operations.

When 11 is the base, the value of the exponent will always be the same as the value of the second-last digit of the expanded number. The last digit is always 1.

PRACTICE EXERCISES

1. a) Describe the pattern 4^2, 4^1, 4^0, 4^{-1}, 4^{-2}....

    b) Express the next number in the pattern as a positive number, and then express it in its expanded form.

2. Evaluate each of the following expressions.

    a) $(-1)^4$ **b)** -1^4 **c)** $-(-3)^3$

    d) $-(3)^3$ **e)** $(-4)^{-3}$ **f)** -6^{-2}

3. The price of a hot dog triples every 6 years. If the hot dog costs $1.50 today, how much will it cost in 60 years?

4. Simplify each of the following expressions and then evaluate for $n = -3$.

a) $\dfrac{n^{-1}}{n^{-2}}$

b) $\left(n^2\right)^2$

c) $\dfrac{\left(n^{-2}\right)^3}{n^{-8}}$

d) $n^5 \times n^{-6}$

5. Simplify each of the following equations using exponent laws. Use "guess-and-test" to solve.

a) $n^5 \div n^3 = 25$

$n^5 - n^3 = 25$
$n^2 = 2^5$
$= 5$

b) $\left(n^3\right)^2 = 729$

$n^6 = 729$
$n = 3$

c) $n^8 \times n^{-12} = \dfrac{1}{256}$

$n^{-4} = \dfrac{1}{256}$

6. Using a calculator, find the first nine values with a base of 6. Then, by examining the last two digits of these numbers, determine the last two digits of 6^{20}.

Lesson 5 USING EXPONENT LAWS TO SIMPLIFY QUESTIONS INVOLVING COEFFICIENTS AND VARIABLES AND TO EVALUATE COMPLEX NUMERICAL QUESTIONS

Exponent laws apply to variables in the same way as they do to numbers.

A **coefficient** is a number that is being multiplied by a variable.

In the previous lessons, you simplified questions that had coefficients of one. In this lesson, you will be performing the indicated operation on the coefficients as well as following the appropriate exponent laws when simplifying the variables.

If you are multiplying two terms made up of coefficients and variables, multiply the coefficients and add the exponents of the variables that have common bases.

If you are dividing two terms made up of coefficients and variables, divide the coefficients and subtract the exponents of the variables that have common bases.

Example 1

Simplify the expression $\left(5x^2y^3\right)\left(6x^4y^2\right)$.

Solution

You should simplify in parts, remembering to carry out the indicated operation on the coefficients.

$$5 \times 6 \times x^2 \times x^4 \times y^3 \times y^2 = 30 \times x^{2+4} \times y^{3+2}$$

$$5 \times 6 \times x^2 \times x^4 \times y^3 \times y^2 = 30x^6y^5$$

Example 2

Simplify the expression $\dfrac{12x^5y^{-3}}{4x^4y^{-4}}$.

Solution

$$\frac{12x^5y^{-3}}{4x^4y^{-4}} = \frac{12}{4} \times x^{5-4} \times y^{-3-(-4)} = 3xy$$

Example 3

Simplify the expression $\left(\dfrac{m^3}{n^4}\right)^5$.

Solution

$$\left(\frac{m^3}{n^4}\right)^5 = \frac{m^{3\times5}}{n^{4\times5}}$$

$$= \frac{m^{15}}{n^{20}}$$

Example 4

Simplify the expression $\dfrac{42x^{-2}y^5}{6x^4y}$.

Solution

$$\frac{42x^{-2}y^5}{6x^4y} = 7x^{-2-4}y^{5-1}$$

$$= 7x^{-6}y^4$$

Example 5

Simplify and evaluate the expression $\dfrac{5^3}{5^2} \times \dfrac{4^6 \times 4^{-2}}{\left(4^2\right)^2}$.

Solution

$$\frac{5^3}{5^2} \times \frac{4^6 \times 4^{-2}}{\left(4^2\right)^2} = 5 \times \frac{4^4}{4^4}$$

$$= 5 \times 4^0$$

$$= 5 \times 1$$

$$= 5$$

PRACTICE EXERCISES

1. Simplify each of the following expressions.

a) $\left(x^{-3}\right)^2$

x^{-6}

$\dfrac{1}{x^6}$

b) $\dfrac{m^2 n^3}{mn^{-2}}$

$m^{(2-1)}n^{3+2}$

mn^5

c) $\dfrac{x^4 y^7 z^{-3}}{x^2 y^{-5} z^2}$

$\dfrac{x^{4-2} y^{7+5}}{z^{2+3}}$

$\dfrac{x^2 y^{12}}{z^5}$

d) $\left(4g^3 h^5\right)\left(-5g^{-4} h^3\right)$

$-20g^{-1}h^8$

e) $\left(3g^{-5} h^5\right)\left(5g^{-4} h^3\right)$

$15g^{-9}h^8$

f) $\left(ab^{-3}\right)^{-5}$

$a^{-5}b15$

g) $\dfrac{-36a^5 b^{-3}}{-12a^6 b^{-5}}$

$-\dfrac{3a^{-1}b^{-8}}{1}$

$+3a^{-1}b^2$

h) $\left(\dfrac{m^2 n^{-3}}{m^4 n}\right)^2$

$\dfrac{m^4 n^{-6}}{m^8 n^2}$

$m^{-4}n^{-8}$

i) $\left(6x^2 y^{-4}\right)\left(-12y^5\right)$

$-72x^2 y^9$

j) $\dfrac{12a^3 b^{-3}}{-18a^5 b^2}$

$-\dfrac{2a^{-2}b^{-1}}{3}$

$\dfrac{-2a^{-2}b^{-1}}{3} = \dfrac{-2}{3a^2 b^1}$

2. Simplify and evaluate each of the following expressions.

a) $\dfrac{2^5}{2^{-2}} \times \dfrac{2^{-4}}{2^2}$

b) $\dfrac{(-3)^9 \times (-3)^{-6}}{(-3)^2}$

c) $\dfrac{3^7}{3^3} \times \dfrac{9^2 \times 9^0}{9^2 \times 9^{-3}}$

PRACTICE QUIZ

1. How many numbers differ between the set of natural numbers and whole numbers?

2. Draw a circle, then a larger one surrounding it. Without using whole or natural numbers, label the larger circle as a number set and the smaller circle as a nested number set.

3. Given that $\sqrt{3}$ is irrational, what can be said about $2\sqrt{3}$?

   A. There is no relationship between $\sqrt{3}$ and $\sqrt[2]{3}$.

   B. $\sqrt[2]{3}$ is also irrational.

   C. $\sqrt[2]{3}$ terminates.

   D. $\sqrt[2]{3}$ is a number set.

4. A particular right-angled triangle has a side of length $\sqrt{9}$ cm and the length of the hypotenuse is $\sqrt{x}$ cm. What is the measure of the third side?
   What is the measure of the third side if $x = 25$ cm?

5. Estimate which of the following numbers is larger, 5 or $\sqrt{26}$, without a calculator. Justify your answer.

6. Evaluate the following problem, using the proper Order of Operations.

$$\frac{(-3)^2}{(|-4|+2)} + 36 \div 4$$

7. Express the following problem as a single base raised to an exponent. Also, express the answer as a decimal, and state the number set that the answer belongs to.

$$3 \div (\sqrt{3} \times \sqrt[3]{3})$$

Lesson 6 SIMPLIFYING RADICALS

At this point, it is possible to rewrite a radical as a base and exponent or give an exact value for many radicals (e.g., $\sqrt{4} = 2$), and estimate those that are not perfect squares or cubes. In this lesson, skills will be introduced that will further allow for the manipulation of radicals.

NOTES

Consider that $\sqrt{2} \times \sqrt{2} = 2$ (from previous knowledge or calculator).

It is also known that $\sqrt{4} = 2$. So, one could express $\sqrt{4}$ as $\sqrt{2 \times 2}$.

From this observation, it is possible to make the correct inference that $\sqrt{2} \times \sqrt{2} = \sqrt{2 \times 2}$

A full investigation into multiplication of radicals is presented in Lesson 5. Here, some basic multiplicative properties are introduced to allow for the simplification of radicals.

Example 1

Evaluate $\sqrt{4} + \sqrt{9}$ by using exact values. Calculate $\sqrt{13}$ and round to one decimal.

Is it true that $\sqrt{4} + \sqrt{9} = \sqrt{13}$?

Solution

From perfect squares, we know that root 4 is equal to 2. Also, root 9 is equal to 3. The sum is 5. By calculator, with rounding, $\sqrt{13} = 3.6$, which is not equal to the sum of 5.

Addition of radicals is dealt with at length in Lesson 6. This example is presented here to underline the idea that just because $\sqrt{2} \times \sqrt{2} = \sqrt{2 \times 2}$, it is **not** also true that $\sqrt{a} + \sqrt{b} = \sqrt{a + b}$.

Example 2

Write $\sqrt{4} \times \sqrt{9}$ with both numbers under the radical sign. Evaluate, and compare this answer with the answer arrived at without combining the numbers.

Solution

$\sqrt{4} \times \sqrt{9} = \sqrt{4 \times 9} = \sqrt{36}$

Since 36 is one of the squares of the first few integers, the answer should be known as 6.

Root 4 is equal to 2, and root 9 is equal to 3. The product of these two integers is 6. So, the answers are the same with or without combining under the radical sign.

Now, observe the reverse process of the example above. A student is given $\sqrt{36}$ and that student remembers that $\sqrt{36} = \sqrt{4 \times 9}$. The student then rewrites this as $\sqrt{4} \times \sqrt{9} = 2 \times \sqrt{9}$. However, for some reason the student forgets the value of root 9, and proceeds to find a calculator.

As well, on occasion throughout the investigation of radicals, the process $\sqrt{\ }$ may be referred to as square root or just root. If the statement says "root 4" it is assumed to mean square root. Just as the radical sign for all n^{th} roots does not list the index 2 for square roots.

NOTES

Consider this intermediate step.

$$\sqrt{36}$$

This is a radical. All numbers are shown under the radical sign. This is called an **Entire Radical**.

$$2\sqrt{9}$$

This is also a radical. Some numbers are shown under the radical sign, and some are out front, acting, in a sense, like coefficients. This is called a **Mixed Radical**. This mixed radical should not be left in this form because root 9 is known. A radical should only be in mixed form if the number under the radical sign is not able to be removed as an exact value.

If the student then remembers that the square root of 9 is 3 and finds that the problem is reduced to the product of 2 times 3, then the final solution of 6 is found. The student has evaluated the radical and there is no longer a radical at all, just a number.

The process of converting from a mixed radical to an entire radical, or evaluating a radical to a number is the next step in the full investigation of radicals.

Example 3

Factor the radicand of the following radical into as many perfect squares as possible. Remove those from the radicand, leaving the radical in mixed radical form.

$$\sqrt{200}$$

Solution

Factoring 200 using as many perfect squares as possible gives the following result:

$$200 = (25)(4)(2)$$

$$\sqrt{200} = \sqrt{25 \times 4 \times 2} = (5)(2)\sqrt{2} = 10\sqrt{2}$$

This is as simplified as the radical gets, and it is the final answer. This is called an exact value, since root 2 is an exact value, but a decimal approximation of this would not be exact. Also, note that when 10 root 2 is written, it is not necessary to write $10 \times \sqrt{2}$.

Example 4

Convert $3\sqrt{2}$ into an entire radical.

Solution

$$3 = \sqrt{9}$$

$$\sqrt{9}\sqrt{2} = \sqrt{18}$$

One way to think of this process is that the 3 is a 3 on the outside of the radical sign, but when placed under the square root sign it is a 9.

CUBE ROOTS AND VARIABLES IN RADICALS

The process of simplifying a radical or going from a mixed to a entire (and vice versa) radical can be applied to cube roots and can be accomplished even when variables are present. Consider the following example.

$$\sqrt[3]{16} = \sqrt[3]{(8)(2)} = 2\sqrt[3]{2}$$

This mixed radical is a cube root, so to remove any number from the radicand, it is necessary to look for factors that are perfect cubes. The cube root of 8, which equals 2, should be familiar by now. The remaining 2 in the radicand cannot be removed as an exact value.

$$\sqrt{x^2} = \sqrt{(x) \times (x)} = \sqrt{x} \times \sqrt{x} = x$$

To reduce a radicand variable, if the root is a square root, look for factors that are squares of the variable and remove them as the variable (to the first power).

$$\sqrt{x^5} = \sqrt{x^2 x^2 x} = (x)(x)\sqrt{x} = x^2 \sqrt{x}$$

This process could have been sped up if the factors were not simply squared values of the variable, but multiples of squares, as seen next:

$$\sqrt{x^5} = \sqrt{x^4 x} = x^2 \sqrt{x}$$

Why does $\sqrt{x^4}$ become x^2? Using the law of exponents and remembering that the square root is $\frac{1}{2}$ as an exponent, this is

$$\left(x^4\right)^{\frac{1}{2}} = x^{\frac{4}{2}} = x^2.$$

For variables in cube root radicals, to remove an a from the radicand, there must be a^3 present. Similarly, for a cube root mixed radical, any number outside of the radical sign will be converted into its cubed value if placed into the radicand.

Example 5

Change the following mixed radical into an entire radical.

$$3ab^2 \sqrt[3]{2}$$

Solution

The 3 will become 3^3 or 27 in the radicand.

The a will become a^3.

The b^2 will become b^6 (since $(b^2)^3 = b^6$.

Rewrite as $\sqrt[3]{(2)(27)a^3b^6}$

$\sqrt[3]{54a^3b^6}$

PRACTICE EXERCISES

1. Does $\sqrt{25} - \sqrt{9} = \sqrt{16}$? Why or why not?

2. Convert $12\sqrt{a}$ into an entire radical.

3. Express $\sqrt{98}$ as a mixed radical.

4. A student is attempting to simplify the factors of the radicand of the radical $\sqrt[3]{(8)(125)(x^4)(b^8)}$ before writing it as a mixed radical.

    The student should not attempt to simplify the factor.
    A. 8
    B. 125
    C. x^4
    D. b^8

5. Evaluate $\sqrt[3]{27x^3 y^9 z^{12}}$.

    $\sqrt{3 \times y^3 z^4}$

6. Change the following radical into a mixed radical, then evaluate it given that $x = 2$. Write the final mixed radical by replacing the radical with its exponential form.

    $\sqrt[3]{54x^6 y}$

Lesson 7 ADDITION AND SUBTRACTION OF RADICALS

In many ways, the addition (and subtraction) of radicals is no more complicated than the addition of $2x + 3x$. The key is to remember that one can only add together like terms. The $2x$ is a like term to the $3x$ and so they add to $5x$. If the addition were $2x + 3y$, then nothing could be done. These are not like.

In radicals, the radicand and the radical sign are equivalent to the x in the statement above. Consider $\sqrt{3}$, $\sqrt{5}$, and $2\sqrt{3}$. This is similar to $x, y, 2x$. One cannot add the root 3 to the root 5. The radicals are not the same. It is possible to add root 3 and 2 root 3. The number outside the radical sign does not need to be the same. Only the radical must be the same (both the radicand and the index must be the same). These are called like radical terms.

The process of simplification of radicals enables like radical terms to be identified. For instance, are $\sqrt{2}$ and $\sqrt{8}$ like terms? They do not appear to be, but remember that $\sqrt{8} = \sqrt{4 \times 2} = 2\sqrt{2}$. So in its simplified form, root 8 is indeed a like radical term for root 2.

Example 1

Express $\sqrt{27} + \sqrt{75}$ as a single radical.

Solution
Simplify the radicals to see if these are like radical terms. If so, add the numbers outside the radical sign, keeping the radicand and radical sign the same.

$\sqrt{27} + \sqrt{75}$

$\sqrt{(9)(3)} + \sqrt{(25)(3)}$

$3\sqrt{3} + 5\sqrt{3}$

$8\sqrt{3}$

Example 2

Simplify $\sqrt{2} - \sqrt[3]{2}$.

Solution
The radicals appear similar because they have the same radicand, but they do not have the same index (i.e., the radical sign is different). It is not possible to add a square root to a cube root as an exact value.

This expression cannot be simplified further.

NOTES

Note that it is possible to calculate approximations for this difference, but unless stated, all work in these lessons involve exact values and not calculator approximations.

More than two radical like terms may be added by following the pattern of adding like terms.

Example 3

Simplify: $3\sqrt[3]{4} - \sqrt{2} - \sqrt[3]{32} - \sqrt{4}$

> *Solution*
>
> The first term cannot be simplified further, and it appears to have no like radical terms in this statement (remember that $\sqrt{4}$ is not a like term to the first term because the first term is a cube root). However, the third term can be simplified to $\sqrt[3]{(8)(4)}$.
>
> $3\sqrt[3]{4} - \sqrt{2} - 2\sqrt[3]{4} - 2$
> $\sqrt[3]{4} - \sqrt{2} - 2$
>
> This is the final simplified form.

Example 4

Two students are trying to trick their math teacher. Each student is supposed to take an equal length of fabric for a class project.
The first student takes a length of fabric represented by $\sqrt{12} + \sqrt{3}$.
This is the proper length. The second student takes $\sqrt{75}$ units of fabric. This is too much fabric, but the student thinks that no one will be the wiser.
How much fabric should the teacher confiscate from the second student to ensure that she has an equal length to the first student?

> *Solution*
>
> The first student has the proper length, which is
> $\sqrt{12} + \sqrt{3} = \sqrt{(4)(3)} + \sqrt{3} = 2\sqrt{3} + \sqrt{3} = 3\sqrt{3}$.
>
> The second student has $\sqrt{75} = \sqrt{(25)(3)} = 5\sqrt{3}$ units of fabric.
>
> So, the teacher should confiscate $2\sqrt{3}$ units from the second student.

The term *addition* is used throughout to refer to the process of adding one radical to another, even if the second radical is a negative. This removes the necessity of continually stating "addition or subtraction of radicals."

SIMPLIFYING

When adding, it is necessary to simplify radicands and, if necessary, to identify like terms. If this is not done, the answer will be incomplete. Simplification must also occur even if the like terms are clearly visible, but not fully simplified.

Example 5

Add $\sqrt{4} + \sqrt{4}$.

Solution

The intermediate answer could be $2\sqrt{4}$, but it then must be converted to $(2)(2) = 4$.

If the root 4 is recognized as 2, the question becomes $2 + 2$, which is 4.

PRACTICE EXERCISES

1. Simplify $2\sqrt{17} + \sqrt{17} - \sqrt{34}$.

2. Add $\sqrt{16} + \sqrt{64}$.

3. When simplified, what does $\sqrt{99} + 2\sqrt{11}$ equal?

    A. It cannot be simplified.

    B. $5\sqrt{11}$

    C. $11\sqrt{11}$

    D. $3 + 2\sqrt{11}$

4. Given that $\sqrt{12} + \sqrt{27} - \sqrt{x} = 0$, solve for the unknown variable, x.

5. Solve $\sqrt{(16)(2)} - \sqrt{(9)(2)}$.

6. Add the square roots of each of the first five natural numbers squared (i.e., the first five perfect squares).

Lesson 8   *MULTIPLICATION AND DIVISION OF RADICALS*

In the previous work on radicals, the following equation was found to be true: $\sqrt{2} \times \sqrt{2} = 2$.

This was also expanded to $\sqrt{2}\sqrt{2} = \sqrt{2 \times 2}$.

The method for multiplication of radicals can be stated as

$$a\sqrt{x} \times b\sqrt{y} = a \times b\sqrt{x \times y}$$

That is, the values outside the radical sign are multiplied as normal, and the radicands are also multiplied, thereby forming a new radicand. This new radicand can often be simplified.

Note that the two radicals to be multiplied must both be square roots or both cube roots, etc. The process of multiplying a square root radical by a cube root radical is beyond the scope of this investigation.

If you are curious as to the method used for the above stated product, the key is to convert to exponential form and then remember that exponents can be added only if their bases are the same.

Example 1

Multiply and simplify $2\sqrt{2} \times 3\sqrt{2}$, if possible.

Solution

The product is found by $(2)(3)\sqrt{(2)(2)} = 6\sqrt{4} = (6)(2) = 12$

Example 2

Simplify $4\sqrt[3]{32} \times 2\sqrt[3]{108}$. Hint: first, reduce the radicands further.

Solution

Note that cube roots are involved. The process will be easier if the radicands are fully simplified before the multiplication takes place.

$4\sqrt[3]{32} \times 2\sqrt[3]{108}$

$4\sqrt[3]{(8)(4)} \times 2\sqrt[3]{(27)(4)}$

$4(2)\sqrt[3]{4} \times 2(3)\sqrt[3]{4}$

$(8)(6)\sqrt[3]{16}$

$48\sqrt[3]{8(2)}$

$96\sqrt[3]{2}$

MULTIPLYING BY BINOMIALS

Multiplying a radical by a binomial follows the same distributive pattern as multiplying a constant by a binomial. Each term within the binomial is multiplied by the radical.

Example 3

Multiply $\sqrt{3}\left(3\sqrt{3}-2\sqrt{2}\right)$.

Solution

By distribution, the $\sqrt{3}$ will be multiplied by each term in the binomial, with the subtraction remaining.

$$1\sqrt{3}\times3\sqrt{3}-1\sqrt{3}\times2\sqrt{2}$$
$$3\left(\sqrt{3}\sqrt{3}\right)-2\left(\sqrt{3}\sqrt{2}\right)$$
$$3(3)-2\left(\sqrt{6}\right)$$
$$9-2\sqrt{6}$$

The final answer cannot be simplified further.

A binomial can also be multiplied by a binomial by following the same distributive method as though radicals were not involved.

Example 4

Expand and simplify $\left(2\sqrt{3}+2\right)\left(3\sqrt{2}-\sqrt{3}\right)$.

Solution

By the known method of multiplication of binomials (distributive), the term $2\sqrt{3}$ will be multiplied by each term in the second binomial. The constant, 2, will also be multiplied by each term in the second binomial. These results will be added.

$$2\sqrt{3}\left(3\sqrt{2}\right)+2\sqrt{3}\left(-\sqrt{3}\right)+2\left(3\sqrt{2}\right)+2\left(-\sqrt{3}\right)$$
$$6\sqrt{6}-2(3)+6\sqrt{2}-2\sqrt{3}$$
$$6\sqrt{6}-2\sqrt{3}+6\sqrt{2}-6$$

Here, the product of a binomial and another binomial produced an expected four terms, and there were no like radical terms to combine. Some products of binomials reduce, and a special case is dealt with next.

THE CONJUGATE BINOMIAL

Recall that in factoring polynomials, the difference of squares binomial was a special case:

$$x^2 - 1 = (x+1)(x-1)$$

The reverse process is $(x+1)(x-1) = x^2 - 1$. This was expanded to the general case of $(x+a)(x-a) = x^2 - a^2$, where x is any variable.

Now, this can also apply to radical expressions.

Example 5

Simplify $\left(\sqrt{2}+1\right)\left(\sqrt{2}-1\right)$.

Solution

Distribute

$$\sqrt{2}\sqrt{2} + \sqrt{2}(-1) + 1\sqrt{2} + 1(-1)$$
$$2 - \sqrt{2} + \sqrt{2} - 1$$
$$2 - 1$$
$$1$$

Notice that in the second step, the two radicals cancel and that in the third step, all that is left is the square of the first term (of each binomial) minus the square of the second term (of either binomial).

The conjugate of a given binomial $(a - b)$ is $(a + b)$ and vice versa. The product is $a^2 - b^2$. The variables a and b can be radicals, variables, or non-radical numbers. This is a very useful when simplifying radical expressions, since the squared values created automatically remove radicals (of a square root value).

Binomial conjugates of square roots are only dealt with at this level. More complex radicals, even those of multiples of two roots, are not examined here.

DIVISION OF RADICALS

At this point in the investigation of radicals, only two types of radical division are dealt with. The first type is a radical of the form $\dfrac{3\sqrt{5}}{\sqrt{2}}$, where there is a monomial radical in the denominator.

The second type is a radical of the form $\dfrac{\sqrt{2}}{\sqrt{2}+1}$, where the denominator is a binomial that can be multiplied by its conjugate to simplify, thereby removing the radical. Note that in each case, the numerator is not limited. It can be a monomial, binomial, or a more complex polynomial.

To deal with the first case, the numerator and denominator are multiplied by the radical in the denominator. The numerator is dealt with as a product of radicals, and the denominator radical sign is removed. See Example 6.

To deal with the second case, the numerator and denominator are multiplied by the conjugate of the denominator. This reduces the denominator to a difference of squares (and removes any radical signs). See Example 7.

Example 6

Simplify $\dfrac{5\sqrt{6}}{2\sqrt{3}}$.

Solution

Multiply the entire fraction by $\sqrt{3}$ (numerator and denominator).

$$\frac{5\sqrt{6}}{2\sqrt{3}}\left(\frac{\sqrt{3}}{\sqrt{3}}\right)$$

$$\frac{5\sqrt{18}}{2(3)}$$

$$\frac{5\sqrt{9\times2}}{6}$$

$$\frac{15\sqrt{2}}{6}$$

$$\frac{5\sqrt{2}}{2}$$

The final form is simplified enough, even though there is still a denominator other than 1; as long as there are no common factors remaining to cancel. It is important to remove the radical from the denominator. The process of removing all radicals from the denominator is called **rationalizing** the denominator.

Example 7

Simplify by rationalizing the expression $\dfrac{\sqrt{3}+1}{\sqrt{3}-1}$.

Solution

The conjugate of the denominator is $\sqrt{3}+1$. Multiply the entire fraction by this to rationalize the denominator.

$$\frac{\sqrt{3}+1}{\sqrt{3}-1}\left(\frac{\sqrt{3}+1}{\sqrt{3}+1}\right)$$

$$\frac{\sqrt{3}\sqrt{3}+1\sqrt{3}+1\sqrt{3}+1}{\sqrt{3}\sqrt{3}+1\sqrt{3}-1\sqrt{3}-1(1)}$$

$$\frac{3+2\sqrt{3}+1}{3-1}$$

$$\frac{4+2\sqrt{3}}{2}$$

$$2+\sqrt{3}$$

The final form, after rationalizing the denominator and simplifying, allows for the denominator to disappear (it is actually 1 of course).

It is possible to remove common factors before any rationalizing. It is also possible to simplify a radical before the rationalization process. The steps may occur in any order, so long as the final form is completely reduced (no common factors to cancel) and no radicals remain in the denominator.

PRACTICE EXERCISES

1. Simplify $2\sqrt{2} \times 3\sqrt{2}$.

2. If $a\sqrt{2} \times 2\sqrt{5} = 8\sqrt{10}$, what is a?

3. Multiply and simplify $12\sqrt{2} \times 2\sqrt{3} \times 2\sqrt{2}$.

4. If the conjugate of $\left(2\sqrt{7} - 3\sqrt{4}\right)$ is multiplied by $2\sqrt{7}$, the final result is

    A. $28 + 12\sqrt{7}$

    B. $28 - 12\sqrt{7}$

    C. $4\sqrt{49} + 6\sqrt{28}$

    D. $4\sqrt{49} - 6\sqrt{28}$

5. Rationalize and simplify the expression $\dfrac{3\sqrt{72}}{2\sqrt{12}}$.

6. Simplify $\dfrac{\sqrt{48}}{2\sqrt{3x}}$ and evaluate, given that $x = 2$.

REVIEW SUMMARY

In this unit, you have learned how to . . .

- classify numbers according to the number sets including:
  Natural numbers
  Whole numbers
  Integers
  Rational numbers
  Irrational numbers
  Real numbers

- use approximate representations of irrational numbers, ensuring that decimals are correctly rounded

- communicate a set of instructions used to solve an arithmetic problem

- perform arithmetic operations on irrational numbers by using appropriate decimal approximations and leaving answers correctly rounded

- use exponent laws for powers with rational exponents including the product, quotient, and power laws

- simplify radicals expressing entire radicals as mixed radicals and vice versa

- add, subtract, multiply, and divide radicals as exact values, leaving the answers fully simplified and rationalized

PRACTICE TEST

1. Which of the following characteristics must a number have in order to be classified as an irrational   number?

    A. The decimal value of the number repeats and terminates.

    B. The decimal value of the number repeats but does not terminate.

    C. The decimal value of the number does not repeat or terminate.

    D. The decimal value of the number does not repeat but does terminate.

2. On a test, there are three circles: one large circle surrounding a smaller one, which surrounds an even smaller one. The innermost (smallest) circle represents the natural numbers. The largest circle represents the integer numbers. What does the middle circle represent? What is this pictorial representation called (i.e., what term applies to one number system inside another)?

3. A student chooses to write a known irrational number ($\sqrt{3}$) as a fraction $\dfrac{\sqrt{3}}{1}$. Why does this form **not** make this irrational number rational?

4. Estimate the value of the following three radicals and place them on a number line.

    $\sqrt{15}$ $\sqrt[3]{9}$ $\dfrac{\sqrt{101}}{2}$

5. A right-angled triangle has a short side defined by the expression $2 + \sqrt{3}$, a longer side of $3 + \sqrt{3}$, and the longest side (hypotenuse) equal to $x + \sqrt{3}$. Without solving, show the steps required to solve a problem that asks for the value of x.

6. Simplify $\left(\dfrac{2}{8}\right)^{-2} - 2 + \left(\dfrac{23}{\sqrt{3}}\right)^{0}$.

$$\dfrac{8}{2^2} = \dfrac{8}{4} = 2 - 2 + 1$$

$$= 1$$

7. Which of the following values, when expressed as a base raised to an exponent, has an exponent equal to 2?

   A. $\sqrt{16}$

   B. $\sqrt[3]{8}$

   C. $2 + 1$

   D. 8

8. Express $\sqrt{27} + \sqrt{12} - \sqrt{75}$ as a single radical.

9. Evaluate $\dfrac{\sqrt{64-16}}{\sqrt{3}}$ by rationalizing.

10. Express $\sqrt{28x^3y^5}$ as a mixed radical.

11. Simplify $\dfrac{\left(\sqrt{3}+1\right)\left(\sqrt{3}-1\right)}{\sqrt{5}+2}$.

NOTES

LINE SEGMENTS AND GRAPHS

When you are finished this unit, you should be able to . . .

- graph linear and non-linear data
- solve problems involving distances between points on a coordinate plane
- solve problems involving the midpoints of line segments
- solve problems involving rise, run, and slopes of line segments
- solve problems using slopes of parallel and perpendicular lines
- determine the equation of a line when given the required information

PREREQUISITE SKILLS AND KNOWLEDGE

Prior to beginning this unit, you should be able to . . .

- apply the Pythagorean theorem to solve problems involving triangles
- plot points on a Cartesian plane
- manipulate an equation to isolate a desired variable
- solve single-variable equations
- classify triangles and rectangles according to side length and angles

Lesson 1 PLOTTING LINEAR AND NON-LINEAR DATA

A common way of organizing data is in a table of values. In such tables, the first column contains the independent or manipulated data and the second column contains the dependent or responding data.

A table of values makes a useful starting point when the data is to be graphed. It provides the information that will be useful when determining the scale and units for the graph.

A determination can be made from the table of values about whether the data that will be graphed is continuous or discrete.

Continuous data includes all values between the measured points. For example, if a child's height is measured to be 105 cm one year and 109 cm the next year, it is understood that during the time in between, the child passed through each of the heights in between.

Discrete data does not include all of the in-between data. For example, if a can of pop costs $1.00, it is assumed that 1.32 cans of pop cannot be purchased for $1.32. It does not make sense to think of partial cans of pop being sold.

When graphing continuous information, the data must be connected to indicate the inclusion of all of the information between the points.

Graphs of discrete points should not have the points connected. The exception is when the range of numbers is large relative to the space between them. For example, with the $1.00 can of pop, it would not be reasonable to graph 1 000 separate points to represent the sale of 1 000 cans of pop.

When the graph of the data forms a straight line, the relationship is said to be linear.

If something other than a straight line is found, the relationship is said to be non-linear.

Example 1

A loom weaves bolts of fabric that are measured in metres.
The following table shows the length (l) in metres that is produced
after given intervals of time(t) in minutes.

t (minutes)	l (metres)
2	10
4	20
6	30
8	40

a) Graph the data.

b) Is this a linear or non-linear relationship?

c) Is $(-2, -10)$ a point on the graph? Explain why or why not.

Solution

a) First, a scale needs to be chosen.

t is the independent variable and will be on the horizontal
axis. All data will be clearly displayed if the axis scale
goes from 0 to 10 minutes.

l is the dependent variable and will be on the vertical axis.
All data will be shown if the scale on the axis goes from
0 to 50 m.

Draw the axes, label the scale, and plot the points.

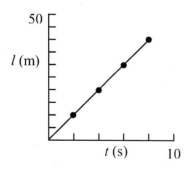

The points should be connected since the data is continuous.
Even though it is not shown on the table of values, there was a
point at 3.5 minutes where a measurable length of fabric
existed.

b) The graph is a straight line so the relationship is linear.

c) $(-2, -10)$ is not a point on the graph. This would mean
that 2 minutes before weaving started, there was -2 m of
fabric complete, which makes no sense.

The data in Example 1 could have been graphed using a graphing calculator. To do this, the following steps must be followed.

Step 1
Data from the table must be entered into the statistics lists.

Step 2
The statistics plot must be turned on.

Step 3
The correct type of graph needs to be selected. The points can be left separate or connected as appropriate.

Step 4
Set the window. This is the graphing calculator's equivalent to choosing and labelling the scale. The minimum, maximum, and scale for each axis must be given. The way to communicate this on paper is in the form

$$X\left[x_{min}, x_{max}, x_{scl}\right] Y\left[y_{min}, y_{max}, y_{scl}\right].$$

Step 5
☐   Select graph

Example 2
State the viewing window that should be used on a graphing calculator to view the graph from Example 1.

Solution

$$X\left[0, 10, 2\right] Y\left[0, 50, 5\right]$$

It should be noted that slight variations in window settings will still produce the correct graph.

228

Example 3

The following table of values shows the height (h) in metres of an object that has been thrown in the air and eventually falls back down.

t (s)	h (m)
0	5
0.5	6.8
1	8.1
1.5	7.0
2	3.4
2.5	0

a) Sketch a graph of the data.
b) Is this a linear or non-linear relationship?
c) What do you expect the height to be when $t = 5$ seconds? Explain.
d) State the calculator window that would correctly display this data.

Solution

a)

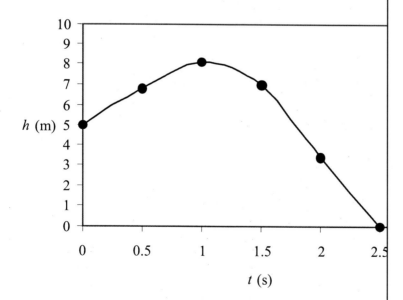

The data should be connected by a line since it is continuous.

b) This data is non-linear.

c) The height at 5 seconds should still be 0, since the object has hit the ground.

d) $X[0, 3, 0.5]\,Y[0, 10, 1]$

Example 4

A school club decides to run a car wash as a fundraiser. The table of values shows their earnings.

Number of Cars (n)	Money Earned ($)
1	5.50
2	11.00
3	16.50
4	22.00
5	27.50
6	33.00
7	38.50
8	44.00

a) Graph the data above.
b) Is this a linear or non-linear relationship?
c) State the calculator window that would correctly display this data.

Solution

a)

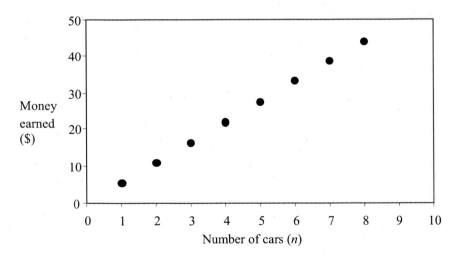

The dots should not be connected because this data is discrete. There is not a case where 5.25 cars are washed.

b) This is a linear relationship.

c) $X[0, 10, 1]\,Y[0, 50, 10]$

PRACTICE EXERCISES

1. Data is graphed and the following graph is the result.

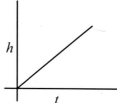

The relationship between the variables on the graph above is
A. linear and continuous
B. non-linear and continuous
C. linear and discrete
D. non-linear and discrete

2. Which of the following window settings would best display the information in the table of values below?

n	c
2	18
4	25
6	32
8	39
10	46

A. $X[-10, 10, 2]Y[-50, 50, 5]$

B. $X[-50, 50, 5]Y[-10, 10, 2]$

C. $X[0, 12, 2]Y[0, 50, 5]$

D. $X[0, 50, 5]Y[0, 12, 2]$

3. State whether each of the following relationships contains continuous or discrete values.
a) Lexi's grandmother is spending the day making jam, and each hour, she makes 5 jars of jam.

b) Each time Stephen's dog goes to the vet, she gets weighed.

c) Stan gets paid for each flyer he delivers.

d) In a 12-hour period, 5 cm of snow falls.

4. Amorita plants a sunflower and measures its growth throughout the summer.

Age (days)	Height (cm)
0	0
10	10
20	45
30	89
40	131
50	157

a) Draw the graph of this relation.

b) Is this relationship linear or non-linear?

c) Describe what is happening with the rate of growth during the 50 days over which the data is recorded.

5. A kennel sells puppies. The following table shows the revenue generated by puppy sales.

Number of Puppies	Revenue ($)
1	400
2	800
3	1 200
4	1 600
5	2 000

a) Draw a graph of this relation.

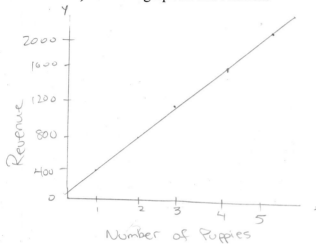

b) Is this relation linear or non-linear?

Linear.

c) State an appropriate window setting for the graphing calculator.

Lesson 2   THE DISTANCE BETWEEN POINTS

NOTES

Consider the points A (–3, 5) and B (1, 2).

In order to find the distance between A and B, we can first graph the two points and draw the line segment connecting them.

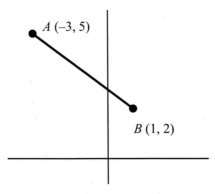

Then, create a right triangle using a vertical and horizontal line segment. The length of these line segments can be determined by counting.

Note that a horizontal and a vertical line could be drawn on the other side as well.

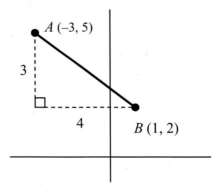

Using the Pythagorean theorem, the distance between A and B can be calculated.

Recall that the Pythagorean theorem is $c^2 = a^2 + b^2$.

$$c^2 = a^2 + b^2$$
$$AB^2 = 3^2 + 4^2$$
$$AB^2 = 9 + 16$$
$$AB^2 = 25$$
$$AB = \sqrt{25}$$
$$AB = 5$$

Notice that only the positive root is considered because we are finding distance.

Example 1

Determine the distance from A (1, −3) to B (4, 1).

Solution

Graph the points and draw the line segment.

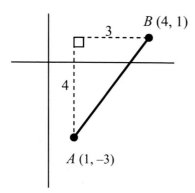

Use the Pythagorean theorem:

$$c^2 = a^2 + b^2$$
$$AB^2 = 4^2 + 3^2$$
$$AB^2 = 16 + 9$$
$$AB^2 = 25$$
$$AB = \sqrt{25}$$
$$AB = 5$$

This method of sketching the points and using the Pythagorean theorem will always work for finding the distance between points. However, it is not always practical and can become time consuming to sketch out points and draw the triangle for each question. Instead, we will generalize a method and a formula.

Instead of looking at a specific case, consider two points, $A(x_1, y_1)$ and $B(x_2, y_2)$.

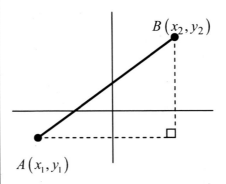

Rather than counting squares to find the horizontal distance, subtract the x-value at A from the x-value at B. Do the same for the vertical distance using the y-values. Let d represent the distance between A and B.

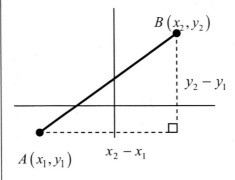

Use the Pythagorean theorem to solve for d.

$$c^2 = a^2 + b^2$$
$$d^2 = (x_2 - x_1)^2 + (y_2 - y_1)^2$$
$$d = \sqrt{(x_2 - x_1)^2 + (y_2 - y_1)^2}$$

This formula is called the distance formula, and since we derived it using general points instead of specific points, we can now use this formula in place of our previous method.

Distance formula:

$$d = \sqrt{(x_2 - x_1)^2 + (y_2 - y_1)^2}$$

Another common way of referring to the distance between A and B is by calling it the length of line segment AB.

Example 3

Find the length of line segment AB where A (3, 6) and B (–2, –1). Leave the answer as an exact value.

Solution

It is helpful to start by assigning variables to the x- and y-coordinates:

$$A\,(3,6) \qquad B\,(-2,-1)$$
$$x_1, y_1 \qquad\quad x_2,\ y_2$$

NOTES

In the distance formula, $(x_2 - x_1)^2$ could be replaced by $(x_1 - x_2)^2$. The answers will be the same since the difference is squared. Similarly, one can find $(y_2 - y_1)^2$ or $(y_1 - y_2)^2$.

Now, substitute into the distance formula:

$$d = \sqrt{(x_2 - x_1)^2 + (y_2 - y_1)^2}$$
$$= \sqrt{(-2 - 3)^2 + (-1 - 6)^2}$$
$$= \sqrt{(-5)^2 + (-7)^2}$$
$$= \sqrt{25 + 49}$$

$$d = \sqrt{74}$$

Example 4

Determine the length of line segment AB. Leave the answer as a reduced radical.

A (–2, 6) B (4, 10)

Solution

$$d = \sqrt{(x_2 - x_1)^2 + (y_2 - y_1)^2}$$
$$= \sqrt{(4 - (-2))^2 + (10 - 6)^2}$$
$$= \sqrt{(6)^2 + (4)^2}$$
$$= \sqrt{36 + 16}$$
$$= \sqrt{52}$$

$$d = 2\sqrt{13}$$

If the line segments in a question form the sides of a triangle, they can be used to classify the triangle as scalene, isosceles, or equilateral.

NOTES

Types of Triangles:
Scalene: 0 equal sides
Isosceles: 2 equal sides
Equilateral: 3 equal sides

In such questions, the lengths of all three sides need to be calculated, and then the definitions of the three types of triangles applied.

Example 5

Classify triangle ABC as scalene, isosceles, or equilateral:
$A(-3, 3)$ $B(3, 5)$ $C(1, -1)$

Solution
Length of AB:
$$d = \sqrt{(3-(-3))^2 + (5-3)^2}$$
$$= \sqrt{(6)^2 + (2)^2}$$
$$= \sqrt{40}$$
$$= 2\sqrt{10}$$

Length of BC:
$$d = \sqrt{(1-3)^2 + (-1-5)^2}$$
$$= \sqrt{(-2)^2 + (-6)^2}$$
$$= \sqrt{40}$$
$$= 2\sqrt{10}$$

Length of CA:
$$d = \sqrt{(-3-1)^2 + (3-(-1))^2}$$
$$= \sqrt{(-4)^2 + (4)^2}$$
$$= \sqrt{32}$$
$$= 4\sqrt{2}$$

Exactly two sides are the same length, so it is an isosceles triangle.

Example 6

The centre of a circle is located at the point (–4, 1). If the circle passes through (2, 7), what is the area of the circle? Round to the nearest tenth.

Solution

Recall that the formula for the area of a circle is $A = \pi r^2$.

First, find the radius. Since the radius is the length of the line segment connecting the centre of the circle to a point on the circle, the distance formula can be used.

$$d = \sqrt{(-4-2)^2 + (1-7)^2}$$
$$= \sqrt{36 + 36}$$
$$= \sqrt{72}$$

Therefore, $r = \sqrt{72}$.

$$A = \pi r^2$$
$$= \pi \left(\sqrt{72}\right)^2$$
$$= \pi (72)$$
$$= 226.2 \text{ square units}$$

PRACTICE EXERCISES

1. Which of the following substitutions into the distance formula is correct for finding the distance between the points $A(1, 2)$ and $B(3, 4)$?

   A. $d = \sqrt{(2-3)^2 + (1-4)^2}$

   B. $d = \sqrt{(4-1)^2 + (3-2)^2}$

   C. $d = \sqrt{(3-1)^2 + (4-2)^2}$

   D. $d = \sqrt{(1-2)^2 + (3-4)^2}$

2. What is the length of the line segment shown below. The answer should be a reduced radical.

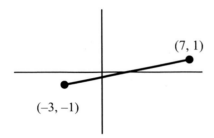

   A. $2\sqrt{5}$

   B. $2\sqrt{6}$

   $d = \sqrt{(7+3)^2 + (1+1)^2}$

   C. 52

   D. $2\sqrt{26}$

3. Determine the lengths of the line segments labelled *AB*. Round your answers to the nearest tenth.

   a) $A(-6, 2)$ $B(2, -1)$

   $$\sqrt{(2+6)^2 + (-1+2)^2} = 8.1$$

   b) $A(12, 40)$ $B(-20, -5)$

   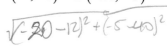

   $$\sqrt{(-20-12)^2 + (-5-40)^2}$$

   57.0

4. The corners of a square garden are located at $(0, 0)$, $(5, -2)$, $(3, -7)$, and $(-5, -2)$.

   a) What is the area of the garden?

   $$\sqrt{(5-0)^2 + (-2-0)^2} = \sqrt{29}$$ 29 units^2

   $$\sqrt{(3-5)^2 + (-7+2)^2} = \sqrt{29}$$

   $$\sqrt{(-5+3)^2 + (-2+7)^2}$$

   b) What is the perimeter of the garden?

   $$4\sqrt{29}$$

   c) The owner wishes to fence the garden with fencing that costs $11.50 per unit. How much will the fencing cost?

   $$\$11.50 \times 4\sqrt{29}$$

5. Classify triangle *ABC* as scalene, isosceles, or equilateral.

   $A(-3, 3)$ $B(3, 2)$ $C(-1, -4)$

Lesson 3   THE MIDPOINT OF THE SEGMENT

The midpoint of a line segment is a point on the line segment that is exactly in the middle of the line segment. In other words, the midpoint is the same distance from each of the two end points of the line segment.

The midpoint of a line segment is normally an ordered pair represented by an uppercase letter *M*.

When the graph of the line segment is given and the endpoints are labelled or obvious, the midpoint can be determined visually or by counting.

Consider the following line segment:

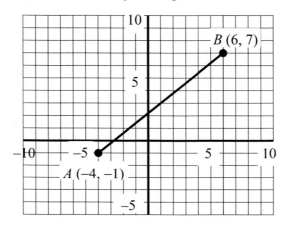

It is fairly easy to locate visually the middle of the line segment at (1, 3). However, if this is not apparent, the horizontal and vertical distance between the points can be counted and cut in half to locate the midpoint.

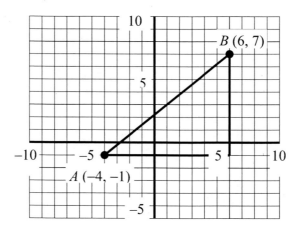

242

Since there are 10 horizontal units between the endpoints, there will be 5 units from either endpoint to the midpoint. Similarly, there are 4 vertical units from either endpoint to the midpoint. From either endpoint, count 5 units horizontally and 4 units vertically.

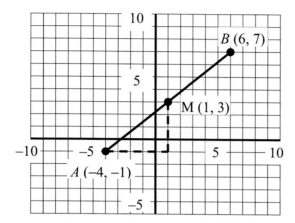

Another way to think of this is to think of the x-coordinate of the midpoint as the arithmetic average of the x-values of the endpoints.

$$x = \frac{-4 + 6}{2}$$
$$x = 1$$

Do the same with the y-coordinate of the midpoint:

$$y = \frac{-1 + 7}{2}$$
$$= 3$$

This leads to the midpoint formula for two endpoints of a line segment, $A(x_1, y_1)$ and $B(x_2, y_2)$:

$$M = \left(\frac{x_1 + x_2}{2}, \frac{y_1 + y_2}{2} \right)$$

Example 1

Determine the midpoint of the two line segments given below.

a)

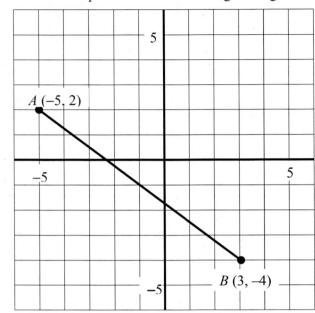

b) A line segment with the endpoints $A(3, -7)$ and $B(-2, 5)$

Solution

a) By inspection or counting, the midpoint is $(-1, -1)$.

Using the midpoint formula:

$$M = \left(\frac{x_1 + x_2}{2}, \frac{y_1 + y_2}{2} \right)$$

$$M = \left(\frac{3-2}{2}, \frac{-7+5}{2} \right)$$

$$M = \left(\frac{1}{2}, -1 \right)$$

The same methods can be altered slightly to find an endpoint if the midpoint and the other endpoint are known.

Example 2

Find the other endpoint, B of AB, given that the coordinates of A are $(-2, 4)$ and the coordinates of the midpoint are $(-5, -1)$.

Solution

Method 1

Sketch the points.

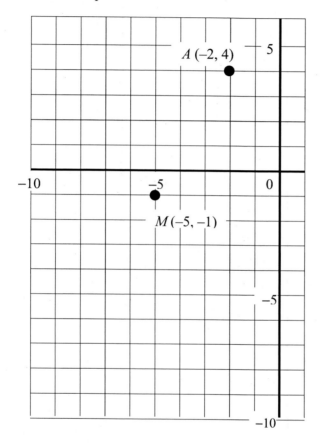

Count the vertical and horizontal distances from A to M. Count the same distances away from the midpoint in the opposite direction.

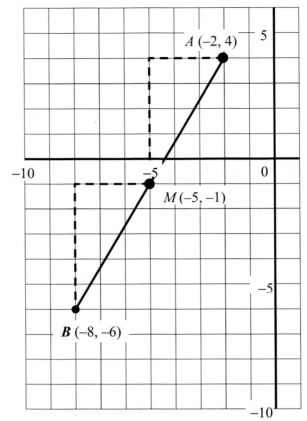

The other endpoint is $B\left(-8,-6\right)$.

Method 2

Using the midpoint formula:

$$M = \left(\frac{x_1 + x_2}{2}, \frac{y_1 + y_2}{2}\right)$$

$$(-5, -1) = \left(\frac{-2 + x_2}{2}, \frac{4 + y_2}{2}\right)$$

Separate into two equations: one for x and one for y:

$$-5 = \frac{-2 + x_2}{2} \qquad\qquad -1 = \frac{4 + y_2}{2}$$

$$-10 = -2 + x_2 \qquad\qquad -2 = 4 + y_2$$

$$-8 = x_2 \qquad\qquad -6 = y_2$$

The other endpoint is at $(-8, -6)$.

In general, if the graph is provided and the endpoints are easy to read, method 1 would be the best to use. In most other cases, method 2 is the best.

Example 3

The line segment CD has a midpoint at $(0, -6)$. The endpoint, C, is at $(2, 1)$. Where is the other endpoint, D?

Solution

$$M = \left(\frac{x_1 + x_2}{2}, \frac{y_1 + y_2}{2} \right)$$

$$(0, -6) = \left(\frac{2 + x_2}{2}, \frac{1 + y_2}{2} \right)$$

Find the *x*-coordinate: Find the *y*-coordinate:

$$0 = \frac{2 + x_2}{2} \qquad\qquad -6 = \frac{1 + y_2}{2}$$

$$0 = 2 + x_2 \qquad\qquad -12 = 1 + y_2$$

$$-2 = x_2 \qquad\qquad -13 = y_2$$

The coordinates of endpoint D are $(-2, -13)$.

The idea of a midpoint can be integrated into problems that model real-life situations or applications of other geometry problems. The methods of solving the problems stay the same.

Example 4

A store is located midway between Stephen's house and Bryce's house.
If the locations of their houses are represented by points $(-6, -1)$ and $(4, 10)$, respectively, then what point represents the store's location?

Solution

$$M = \left(\frac{x_1 + x_2}{2}, \frac{y_1 + y_2}{2} \right)$$

$$M = \left(\frac{-6 + 4}{2}, \frac{-1 + 10}{2} \right)$$

$$M = \left(-1, \frac{9}{2} \right)$$

The store's location is represented by point $\left(-1, \frac{9}{2} \right)$.

The centre of a circle is located at the midpoint of a diameter.

Example 5

One endpoint of a diameter of a circle is at $(-3, 7)$. The centre of a circle is at point $(2, -1)$. Find the other endpoint of the diameter.

Solution

Since M is at point $(2, -1)$, we can use the midpoint formula to find the other endpoint.

$$M = \left(\frac{x_1 + x_2}{2}, \frac{y_1 + y_2}{2} \right)$$

$$(2, -1) = \left(\frac{-3 + x_2}{2}, \frac{7 + y_2}{2} \right)$$

Find the x-coordinate:

$$2 = \frac{-3 + x_2}{2}$$

$$4 = -3 + x_2$$

$$7 = x_2$$

Find the y-coordinate:

$$-1 = \frac{7 + y_2}{2}$$

$$-2 = 7 + y_2$$

$$-9 = y_2$$

The other endpoint is at $(7, -9)$.

Example 6

The vertices of triangle ABC are located at $(-7, 3)$, $(3, 1)$, and $(-1, -5)$, respectively.

a) Determine the midpoints, D, E, and F, of each of the sides of the triangle.

b) Determine the perimeter of triangle DEF that is formed when the midpoints above are connected.

Solution

a) Using the midpoint formula;

$$M = \left(\frac{x_1 + x_2}{2}, \frac{y_1 + y_2}{2} \right)$$

The midpoint of AB:

$$D = \left(\frac{-7 + 3}{2}, \frac{3 + 1}{2} \right)$$

$$D = (-2, 2)$$

The midpoint of BC:

$$E = \left(\frac{3 - 1}{2}, \frac{1 - 5}{2} \right)$$

$$E = (1, -2)$$

The midpoint of CA:

$$F = \left(\frac{-1 - 7}{2}, \frac{-5 + 3}{2} \right)$$

$$F = (-4, -1)$$

b) To find the perimeter of triangle DEF, the length of each side must be found and the lengths added together.

To find the length, use the distance formula.
Length of DE:

$$d = \sqrt{(x_2 - x_1)^2 + (y_2 - y_1)^2}$$
$$= \sqrt{(1 - (-2))^2 + (-2 - 2)^2}$$
$$= \sqrt{(3)^2 + (-4)^2}$$
$$= \sqrt{9 + 16}$$
$$= \sqrt{25}$$
$$d = 5$$

The distance formula is:

$$\sqrt{(x_2 - x_1)^2 + (y_2 - y_1)^2}$$

Length of *EF*:

$$d = \sqrt{(-4-1)^2 + (-1-(-2))^2}$$
$$= \sqrt{(-5)^2 + (1)^2}$$
$$= \sqrt{26}$$
$$d \approx 5.099$$

Length of *FD*:

$$d = \sqrt{(-4-(-2))^2 + (-1-2)^2}$$
$$= \sqrt{(-2)^2 + (-3)^2}$$
$$= \sqrt{4+9}$$
$$= \sqrt{13}$$
$$d \approx 3.606$$

The perimeter of triangle *DEF* is

$$5 + 5.099 + 3.606$$
$$\approx 13.70 \text{ units}$$

PRACTICE EXERCISES

1. Which of the following points is the midpoint of $\overline{AB}$, where A is located at $(4, -7)$ and B is located at $(-6, -3)$?

    A. $M(-5, -1)$

    B. $M(-1, -5)$

    C. $M(5, -2)$

    D. $M(-2, 5)$

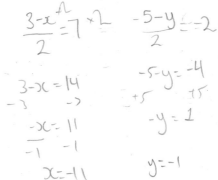

$$\frac{4-6}{2}, \quad \frac{-7-3}{2}$$

$$-1, -5$$

2. The point $(7, -2)$ is the midpoint of line segment AB. If one endpoint is located at $(3, -5)$, where is the other endpoint located?

    A. $\left(2, \dfrac{-7}{2}\right)$

    B. $(1, -11)$

    C. $\left(2, \dfrac{-2}{7}\right)$

    D. $(11, 1)$

$$\frac{3-x}{2} = 7 \times 2 \qquad \frac{-5-y}{2} = -2$$

$$3-x = 14 \qquad -5-y = -4$$
$$-3 \qquad \qquad +5 \qquad +5$$
$$\frac{-x = 11}{-1 \quad -1} \qquad -y = 1$$
$$x = -11 \qquad y = -1$$

3. For each line segment, AB, find the midpoint.

    a)

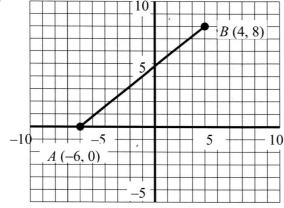

$A(-6, 0)$

$B(4, 8)$

    b) $A(12, -7)$ and $B(-2, 11)$

$$\frac{12+2}{2} \qquad \frac{-7-11}{2} \qquad 7, -9$$

    c) $A\left(\dfrac{3}{2}, 5\right)$ and $B\left(-\dfrac{5}{2}, -8\right)$

4. Point $M(-1, 5)$ is the midpoint of line segment AB and line segment CD. If A is located at $(-3, -2)$ and C is located at $(4, 1)$, what are the coordinates of points B and D?

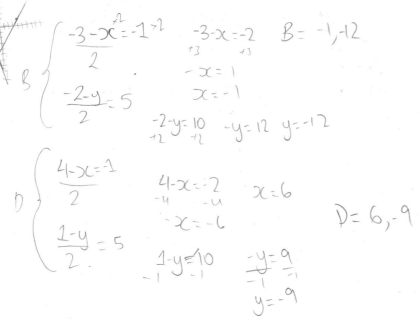

5. Find the distance between the midpoint of $\overline{AB}$ and point C, where A is at $(-10, 3)$, B is at $(4, 7)$, and C is at $(0, -2)$.

$$\frac{-10+4}{2} \quad \frac{3+7}{2}$$

$$-3, 5$$

$$\sqrt{(0+3)^2 + (-2-5)^2} = \sqrt{58} = 7.6 \text{ units}$$

Lesson 4 SLOPE

The slope of a line segment is a measure of the line segment's steepness. That is, a comparison between the vertical change and the horizontal change. The vertical change is called the rise. The horizontal change is called the run. Slope is normally represented by the lowercase letter *m*.

$$m = \frac{\text{rise}}{\text{run}}$$

Consider the following line segment, *AB*:

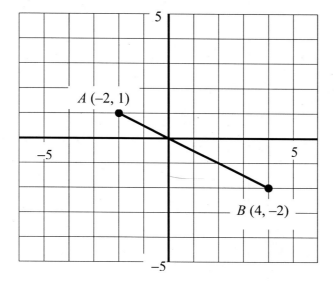

The use and sum of line segment *AB* can be determined by counting.

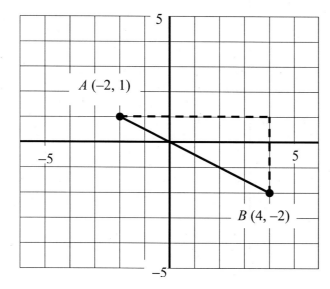

NOTES

Rise: 3 units down. Since the line is going down, the rise is negative.

Run: 6 units right

$$m = \frac{\text{rise}}{\text{run}}$$

$$= \frac{-3}{6}$$

The slope is $-\dfrac{1}{2}$.

All line segments that are going upward from left to right have a positive slope:

All line segments that are going downward from left to right have a negative slope:

The greater the slope (regardless of its sign), the steeper the line.

Since horizontal lines have a rise of zero, they have a slope of zero.

$$m = \frac{0}{\text{any number}}$$

$$= 0$$

Since vertical lines have a run of zero, they have a slope that is undefined.

$$m = \frac{\text{any number}}{0}$$

m is undefined

It is not always convenient to count the rise and run of a line segment.
In such cases, it is useful to have a formula that allows the slope to be calculated given the coordinates of the endpoints of the line segments.

Consider line segment AB:

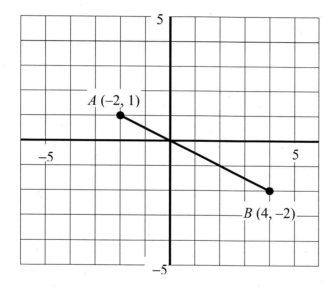

Instead of counting, the rise can be determined by subtracting the y-coordinates:

$$\text{rise} = y_2 - y_1$$

$$= -2 - 1$$

$$= -3$$

NOTES

The run can be determined by subtracting the x-coordinates:

$$\text{run} = x_2 - x_1$$

$$= 4 - (-2)$$

$$= 6$$

$$\text{slope} = \frac{\text{rise}}{\text{run}}$$

$$= \frac{-3}{6} \text{ or } \frac{-1}{2}$$

This method can be summarized into a single formula called the **slope formula**.

$$m = \frac{y_2 - y_1}{x_2 - x_1}$$

Example 1

Determine the slope of the following line segments. Which is steeper?

a) $A(-1, 7)$ $B(4, -3)$ **b)** $A(-20, 3)$ $B(-4, -5)$

A slope of -2 can be thought of as $\frac{-2}{1}$; this is a rise of -2 and a run of 1.

Solution

a) $m = \dfrac{y_2 - y_1}{x_2 - x_1}$

$m = \dfrac{-3 - 7}{4 - (-1)}$

$= \dfrac{-10}{5}$

$= -2$

b) $m = \dfrac{y_2 - y_1}{x_2 - x_1}$

$m = \dfrac{-5 - 3}{-4 - (-20)}$

$= \dfrac{-8}{16}$

$= -\dfrac{1}{2}$

Since 2 is larger than $\dfrac{1}{2}$, the line segment in **a** is steeper than the segment in **b**.

It should be noted that in Example 1, both slopes were reduced to lowest terms. This should always be done. It makes it much easier for comparison purposes.

Points that are on the same line are called **collinear**. Since the slope of a straight line is always the same, the calculated slopes between any pair of collinear points will be equal. This provides a useful tool for determining if points lie on the same line.

Example 2

Are the following points collinear?

$$A(4, -5) \quad B(6, -2) \quad C(10, 4)$$

Solution

Slope of AB

$$m = \frac{y_2 - y_1}{x_2 - x_1}$$

$$= \frac{-2 - (-5)}{6 - 4}$$

$$= \frac{3}{2}$$

Slope of BC

$$m = \frac{y_2 - y_1}{x_2 - x_1}$$

$$= \frac{4 - (-2)}{10 - 6}$$

$$= \frac{6}{4} = \frac{3}{2}$$

Since the points lie along the same line, it is useful to use a common point when determining the slope.

Since the slopes are equal, the points are collinear.

The slope formula can be used to find the x- or y-coordinate of a point if the other coordinate, the slope, and the other point are all known.

Example 3

A line segment has a slope of $\dfrac{3}{4}$. If one endpoint is $A(4, -2)$ and the other endpoint is $B(x, 1)$, what is x?

Solution

$$m = \frac{y_2 - y_1}{x_2 - x_1}$$

Substitute all known values and variables:

$$\frac{3}{4} = \frac{1 - (-2)}{x - 4}$$

NOTES

Solve for x:

$$3(x-4) = 4(1-(-2))$$
$$3x - 12 = 12$$
$$3x = 24$$
$$x = 8$$

The x-coordinate is 8.

Another way of solving this question is to sketch the graph and count using the rise and run of the slope until the given y-coordinate is reached. The x-coordinate can be read off the graph.

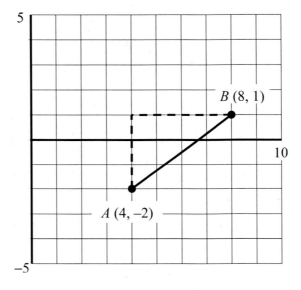

Example 4

Given a line that passes through R (5, –6) and has a slope of $-\dfrac{2}{7}$, determine another point, T, that the line passes through.

Solution

(–2, –4) or (12, –8) depending if $m = \dfrac{-2}{7}$ or $\dfrac{2}{-7}$ used.

If $m = \dfrac{-2}{7}$, then point T could be $(5+7, -6-2) = (12, -8)$.

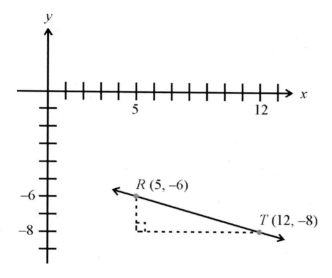

If $m = \dfrac{2}{-7}$, then point T could be $(5-7, -6+2) = (-2, -4)$.

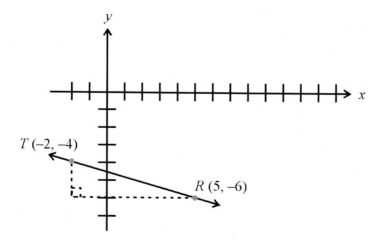

PRACTICE EXERCISES

1. Which of the following slopes is the steepest?

   A. $\dfrac{1}{2}$

   B. $\dfrac{4}{6}$ $\dfrac{2}{3}$

   C. $\dfrac{10}{3}$

   D. 2

2. Which of the following statements is true?
   A. A line with a slope of 0 is vertical.
   B. A line that rises upward from left to right has a negative slope.
   C. A line with a slope of 0 is horizontal.
   D. A line that has a positive slope is going downward from left to right.

3. Find the slope of line segment *AB* in each of the following questions.

   a)

   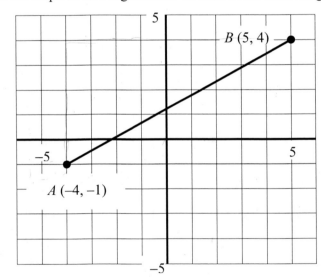

   $\dfrac{5}{9}$

b) $A(3, -2)$ $B(12, 1)$

$$\frac{1+2}{12-3} = \frac{3}{9} = \frac{1}{3}$$

$$m = \frac{y_2 - y_1}{x_2 - x_1}$$

$$\frac{1+2}{12-3} = \frac{3}{9} = \frac{1}{3}$$

c) $A(2, 7)$ $B(-2, 7)$

$$\frac{7-7}{-2-2} = \frac{0}{-4}$$

$$m = \frac{y_2 - y_1}{x_2 - x_1}$$

$$\frac{7-7}{-2 \neq 2} = \frac{0}{-4} = 0$$

d) $A(-5, 1)$ $B(-5, 4)$

$$\frac{4-1}{-5+5} = \frac{3}{0} = \text{undefined}$$

$$\frac{4-1}{-5+5} = \text{error}$$

4. Determine whether or not the following sets of points are collinear.

   a) $A(-4, 2)$ $B(-1, 4)$ $C(5, 8)$

AB $\dfrac{4-2}{-1+4} = \dfrac{2}{3}$

AC $\dfrac{8-2}{5+4} = \dfrac{6}{9} = \dfrac{2}{3}$

AB $BC = \dfrac{8-4}{5+1} = \dfrac{4}{6} = \dfrac{2}{3}$

COLLINEAR

   b) $A(10, 0)$ $B(-2, 4)$ $C(-8, 5)$

$AB = \dfrac{4-0}{-2-10} = \dfrac{4}{-12} = -\dfrac{1}{3}$

$BC = \dfrac{5-4}{-8+2} = \dfrac{1}{-6}$

NOT COLLINEAR

5. Point $A(1, -5)$ is on a line with a slope of $-\dfrac{3}{2}$. Find another point on this line.

6. Point $A(-4, 7)$ is on a line with a slope of $\dfrac{1}{2}$. Point $B(10, y)$ is also on this line. Algebraically determine the value of y.

$$\frac{y - 7}{10 + 4} = \frac{1}{2}$$

$$14 \cdot 7 = 7$$
$$10 + 4 = 14$$

$$2(y - 7) = 10 + 4$$

$$2y - 14 = 14$$
$$+14 \quad +14$$

$$\frac{2y}{2} = \frac{28}{2}$$

$$y = 14$$

Lesson 5 *SLOPES OF PARALLEL AND PERPENDICULAR LINES*

Recall that parallel lines are straight lines that do not meet; they remain the same distance apart.

Consider the following graph of two parallel lines:

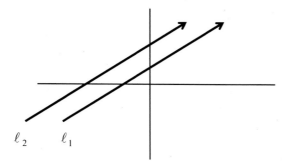

In order to stay parallel, the lines must rise the same amount and run the same amount over the same space. In other words, they have equal slopes.

Conversely, lines with equal slopes are parallel.

Recall that perpendicular lines are lines that meet at a 90° angle.
Consider the following perpendicular lines:

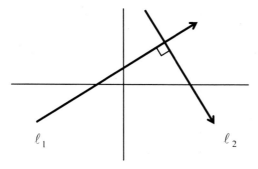

In order to be perpendicular, l_2, must have a slope that is the negative reciprocal of l_1. This means that the slope of one line is multiplied by a negative. The reciprocal is than taken to get the slope of the other line, which is perpendicular.

The reciprocal of an integer, a, is $\dfrac{1}{a}$. The reciprocal of a fraction, $\dfrac{a}{b}$, is $\dfrac{b}{a}$.

Example 1

a) Find the slope of a line that is parallel to the lines with the following slopes.

i) $m = -\dfrac{2}{3}$ ii) $m = 3$

b) Find the slope of a line that is perpendicular to the lines with the following slopes.

i) $m = -\dfrac{2}{3}$ ii) $m = 5$

Solution

a) Since the lines are parallel, the slopes are equal.

i) $m = -\dfrac{2}{3}$ ii) $m = 3$

b) Since the lines are perpendicular, the slopes are negative reciprocals.

i) $m = \dfrac{3}{2}$ ii) $m = -\dfrac{1}{5}$

If the slope of the original line is not given directly, it must be determined before finding the slopes of parallel and perpendicular lines.

Example 2

The points A (2, –6) and B (4, –3) lie on a line.

a) Find the slope of a line parallel to this line.

b) Find the slope of a line perpendicular to this line.

Solution

First, find the slope of the original line.

$$m = \frac{-3-(-6)}{4-2} = \frac{3}{2}$$

a) The slope of the parallel line is equal to the original slope:

$\dfrac{3}{2}$

b) The slope of the perpendicular line is the negative reciprocal: $-\dfrac{2}{3}$.

The ability to classify lines as parallel or perpendicular is helpful when classifying geometric shapes such as triangles, parallelograms, and rectangles.

Consider the following triangle:

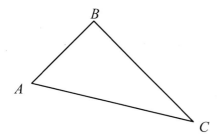

If asked whether or not this is a right triangle, the slopes of $\overline{AB}$ and $\overline{BC}$ should be determined. If they are negative reciprocals, it is a right triangle. If not, it is not a right triangle.

Right Triangle: contains one right angle

Consider the following quadrilateral:

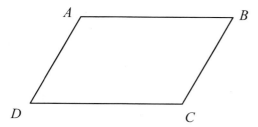

Rectangle: contains 4 right angles and opposite sides are parallel

Parallelogram: opposite sides are parallel

To determine whether or not it is a parallelogram, determine the slopes of $\overline{AB}$, $\overline{BC}$, $\overline{CD}$, and $\overline{DA}$. If the slope of $\overline{AB}$ is equal to the slope of $\overline{CD}$ and if the slope of $\overline{BC}$ is equal to the slope of $\overline{DA}$, then the figure is a parallelogram.

A quadrilateral refers to any four-sided polygon.

Example 3

Is triangle ABC a right triangle?

A (5, 8) B (0, 5) C (3, 0)

Solution

Sketch the triangle.

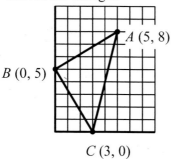

The only angle that looks like it could be a right angle is the angle at B.

Slope of $\overline{AB}$:

$$m = \frac{y_2 - y_1}{x_2 - x_1}$$

$$m = \frac{8 - 5}{5 - 0}$$

$$m = \frac{3}{5}$$

Slope of $\overline{BC}$:

$$m = \frac{0 - 5}{3 - 0} = -\frac{5}{3}$$

Since the slope of $\overline{BC}$ is the negative reciprocal of the slope of $\overline{AB}$, the line segments are perpendicular. This means that the triangle is a right triangle.

Another thing to note about the slopes of perpendicular lines is that their product is –1. The only exception to this is the case of a vertical line and a horizontal line. The product of their slopes is undefined.

Example 4

For each of the following slopes, determine the slope of a perpendicular line segment. Then, find the products of the two slopes.

a) $m = \dfrac{7}{6}$ b) $m = -2$ c) $m = 0$

Solution

a) Slope of perpendicular line: $-\dfrac{6}{7}$

Product of slopes: -1

b) Slope of perpendicular line: $\dfrac{1}{2}$

Product of slopes: $(-2)\left(\dfrac{1}{2}\right) = -1$

c) Slope of perpendicular: undefined
Product of slopes: undefined

Slope concepts can be combined with those involving distance and midpoint in order to classify geometric shapes.

Example 5

Given the coordinates of the vertices of a quadrilateral, describe how to determine what kind of quadrilateral it is.

Solution

Determine the lengths and slopes of all four sides. If opposite sides are parallel, then the object is a parallelogram. Further, if the adjacent sides are perpendicular, then the parallelogram is a rectangle. If the sides are equal in length, then the rectangle is a square.

If the above is true, except for the adjacent sides being perpendicular, then the shape is a rhombus.

PRACTICE EXERCISES

1. Complete the chart below.

Slope of l	Slope of line parallel to l	Slope of line perpendicular to l
$\dfrac{5}{7}$	$\dfrac{5}{7}$	$-\dfrac{7}{5}$
$-\dfrac{3}{5}$	$-\dfrac{3}{5}$	$\dfrac{5}{3}$
4	4	$-\dfrac{1}{4}$
$-\dfrac{1}{3}$	$-\dfrac{1}{3}$	3
0	0	0

2. Which of the following slopes is from a line that is perpendicular to the line segment AB, where A is $(-10, 2)$ and B is $(4, 8)$?

   A. $m = -\dfrac{3}{7}$

   B. $m = -\dfrac{7}{3}$

   C. $m = \dfrac{7}{3}$

   D. $m = \dfrac{3}{7}$

   $$\frac{8-2}{4+10} = \frac{6}{14} = \frac{3}{7}$$

3. Which of the following line segments is parallel to AB, where A is located at $(-13, -1)$ and B is located $at (7, 3)$?

   A. $C(1, 2)$ $D(2, 7)$

   B. $C(0, 3)$ $D(5, 4)$

   C. $C(2, 9)$ $D(3, 4)$

   D. $C(1, 8)$ $D(5, 4)$

   $$A \quad \frac{3+1}{7+13} = \frac{4}{20} = \frac{1}{5}$$

4. Determine whether or not triangle *ABC* is a right triangle.

$A\ (-5, -2), B\ (2, 4), C\ (3, -1)$

$m\overline{AB} \cdot \dfrac{4+2}{2+5} = \dfrac{6}{7}$

$m\overline{BC}\ \dfrac{-1-4}{3-2} = \dfrac{-5}{1}$

NOT RIGHT TRIANGLE

5. Line segment *CD* is perpendicular to line segment *AB* and *D* lies on the *x*-axis. The coordinates of the other points are *A* (–2, 1), *B* (3, 3), and *C* (1, 5). Determine the coordinates of *D*.

$m = -\dfrac{5}{2}$

$\dfrac{3-1}{3+2} = \dfrac{2}{5}$

$x-$

PRACTICE QUIZ

1. The following graph represents a relationship that is

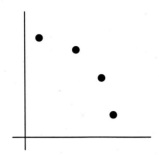

    A. discrete and linear
    B. discrete and non-linear
    C. continuous and linear
    D. continuous and non-linear

2. The slope of a horizontal line is
    A. 0
    B. 1
    C. undefined
    D. negative

3. The distance between points $A(3, -5)$ and $B(1, -2)$ is

    A. $\sqrt{13}$ units
    B. $\sqrt{65}$ units
    C. 13 units
    D. 65 units

4. A particular line segment has endpoints at $A(-3, 4)$ and $B(-7, 8)$.

    a) Find the slope of the line segment.

$$\frac{8-4}{7+3} = \frac{4}{-4} = -1$$

    b) Find the midpoint of the line segment.

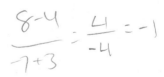

$$\sqrt{(-7+3)^2 + (8-4)^2} = 4\sqrt{2} = 5.7$$

5. A line segment has a midpoint at $M(-7, 1)$. If one endpoint is at $A(1, -3)$, then what are the coordinates of the other end point, B?

$$\frac{1+x}{2} = -7 \qquad \frac{-3+y}{2} = 1$$

$$1 + x = -14 \qquad -3 + y = 2$$
$$\underline{-1 \quad -1} \qquad \underline{+3 \quad +3}$$
$$x = -13 \qquad y = 5$$

6. The points $(2, -10)$ and $(8, y)$ are on a line that has a slope of $-\dfrac{1}{3}$. What is the value of y?

$$\frac{y+10}{8-2} = -\frac{1}{3}$$

$$3(y+10) = 8-2 \qquad \frac{3y}{3} = \frac{-24}{3}$$

$$3y + 30 = 6 \qquad y = -8$$

7. A diameter of a circle has endpoints at $(2, -11)$ and $(6, -3)$.

a) Find the centre of the circle.

$$\frac{2+6}{2} \quad , \quad \frac{-11-3}{2}$$

$$4, -7$$

b) Find the circumference of the circle to the nearest hundredth of a unit.

8. A line segment passes through the points $A(-2, 6)$ and $B(4, -3)$. Find the slope of a line perpendicular to AB.

Lesson 6 *THE EQUATION OF A LINE $y = mx + b$*

Unlike a line segment, a line continues infinitely in both directions. Its slope and its location on a Cartesian plane can uniquely define a line. Any single point on the line defines the line's location on the plane.

The y-intercept is the point where the line crosses the y-axis.

Although any point is sufficient to describe the line's location, this lesson is restricted to those cases where the point is the y-intercept of the line.

There are two forms of linear equations that are of interest.

Standard Form: $Ax + By + C = 0$, where A, B, and C are integers.

The equation of a line is $y = mx + b$.

Slope y-intercept form: $y = mx + b$

When graphing lines, the slope y-intercept form is particularly useful.
This is because the equation is in a form that immediately provides all of the information needed to graph the line.
In the form $y = mx + b$, m is the slope and b is the y-intercept.

Example 1
State the slope and y-intercept for the line defined by the following equation:

$$y = -\frac{1}{2}x + 3$$

Note that a slope of $-\frac{1}{2}$ can be thought of as either $\frac{-1}{2}$ or $\frac{1}{-2}$.

Solution

Slope: $m = -\frac{1}{2}$

y-intercept: $b = 3$

In most cases, the equation must first be manipulated in order to isolate y.

Example 2

Arrange the following equations into $y = mx + b$ form and state the slope and y-intercept.

a) $3x + y = 5$ **b)** $4x - 2y + 8 = 0$

Solution

a) $3x + y = 5$
$$y = -3x + 5$$
$$m = -3$$
$$b = 5$$

b) $4x - 2y + 8 = 0$
$$-2y = -4x - 8$$
$$y = 2x + 4$$
$$m = 2$$
$$b = 4$$

As previously stated, the primary use of this form of the equation of a line is for graphing purposes.

Once the slope and y-intercept are known, the graph can be drawn following these steps:

Step 1

Plot the y-intercept.

Step 2

From the y-intercept, count the rise and run of the slope to locate a second point.

Step 3

Draw a line passing through both points.

Note the a slope of $\frac{3}{4}$ can also be thought of as $\frac{-3}{-4}$.

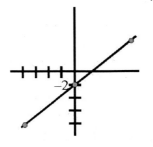

Example 3

Graph the following line.

$$y = \frac{3}{4}x - 2$$

Solution

$$m = \frac{3}{4}$$

$$b = -2$$

Step 1

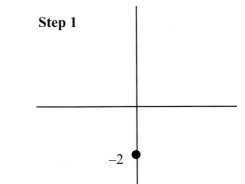

Step 2

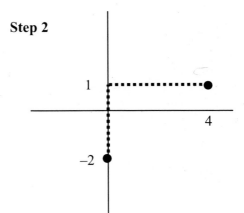

Step 3

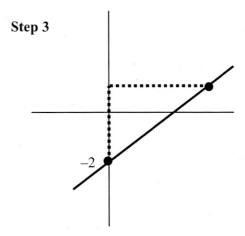

Example 4

Graph the line described by the equation
$3x + 2y - 8 = 0$.

Solution

Rearrange the equation into $y = mx + b$ form.

$3x + 2y - 8 = 0$

$2y = -3x + 8$

$y = -\dfrac{3}{2}x + 4$

$m = -\dfrac{3}{2}$, which can be used as $\dfrac{-3}{2}$ or $\dfrac{3}{-2}$

$b = 4$

Step 1

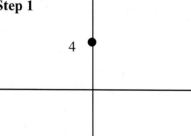

Step 2

Step 3

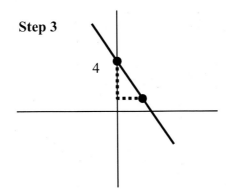

This process also works in reverse. The equation of a line can be produced from a graph if the slope and the *y*-intercept can be determined from the graph.

Example 5

Given the following graph of a line, write the equation of the line.

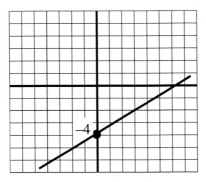

Solution

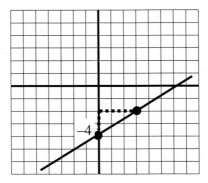

y-intercept: $b = -4$

The slope can be found by counting the rise and run to another readable point.

Rise: 2

Run: 3

$$m = \frac{2}{3}$$

Since m and b are known, they can now be substituted into the formula $y = mx + b$.

$$y = \frac{2}{3}x + (-4)$$

$$y = \frac{2}{3}x - 4$$

Often, the question will ask that the equation be left in standard form. This means manipulating it from $y = mx + b$ to the $Ax + By + C = 0$ form.

Since A, B, and C all have to be integers, the first step should be the removal of any denominators. Next, all terms need to be removed from the right, leaving only 0. Last, ensure that the terms on the left are in the correct order.

Example 6

Change the equation from Example 5 into standard form.

Solution

$$y = \frac{2}{3}x - 4$$

Multiply both sides of the equation by 3 in order to eliminate the denominator.

$$3y = 3\left(\frac{2}{3}x\right) - 3(4)$$

$$3y = 2x - 12$$

Remove all terms from the right side, and arrange them in the correct order on the left side.

$$3y = 2x - 12$$

$$-2x + 3y + 12 = 0$$

It is a standard convention for the numerical coefficient of the x term to be positive. This can be achieved by multiplying both sides by -1.

$$-1(-2x) + -1(3y) + -1(12) = -1(0)$$

$$2x - 3y - 12 = 0$$

Example 7

Write the equation of the line that has a y-intercept of 5 and a slope of $-\dfrac{1}{4}$ in standard form.

Solution

$m = -\dfrac{1}{4}$

$b = 5$

$y = mx + b$

$y = -\dfrac{1}{4}x + 5$

$4(y) = 4\left(-\dfrac{1}{4}x\right) + 4(5)$

$4y = -x + 20$

$x + 4y - 20 = 0$

HORIZONTAL AND VERTICAL LINES

The equations of horizontal lines are always in the form $y = b$, where b is the y-intercept. Since the slope of a horizontal line is 0, $y = 0x + b$ becomes $y = b$.

The equation $y = 2$ has the following graph:

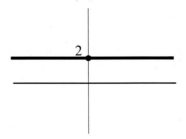

It is a horizontal line passing through the y-axis at 2.

Similarly, the equations of vertical lines have the form $x = a$, where a is the x-intercept.

The equation $x = -5$ has the following graph:

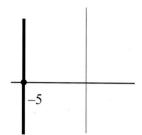

-5

Example 8

a) Write the equation of the following graph.

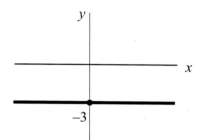

y

x

-3

b) Sketch the graph of $x = 6$.

Solution

a) Since the line is horizontal, the equation has the form $y = b$.
$b = -3$, so the equation is $y = -3$

b) Since the equation is in the form $x = a$, the line is vertical.
The line will have an x-intercept of 6.

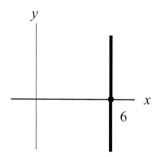

y

x

6

PRACTICE EXERCISES

1. What is the slope of the line with the equation $5x - 2y = 6$?

    A. -3

    B. $-\dfrac{5}{2}$

    C. $\dfrac{5}{2}$

    D. 3

$$\dfrac{-2y}{-2} = \dfrac{-5x + 6}{-2}$$

$$y = \dfrac{5}{2}x + 6$$

2. What is the y-intercept of the line with the equation $x - 3y + 3 = 0$?

    A. -1

    B. $-\dfrac{1}{3}$

    C. $\dfrac{1}{3}$

    D. 1

$$\dfrac{-3y}{-3} = \dfrac{-x - 3}{-3 \quad 3}$$

$$y = \dfrac{x}{3} + 1$$

3. Write the equation of a line with a slope of -4 and a y-intercept of $\dfrac{1}{2}$.

$$y = mx + b$$

$$y = -4x + \dfrac{1}{2}$$

4. Write the equation of a line with a slope of $\dfrac{7}{2}$ and a y-intercept of -5 in standard form.

$$y = \frac{7}{2}x - 5$$

5. Sketch a graph of the lines defined by the following equations.

a) $y = -\dfrac{3}{5}x + 1$

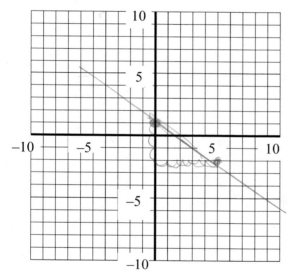

b) $5x - 2y + 6 = 0$

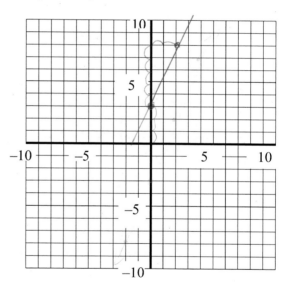

$$\frac{-2y}{-2} = \frac{-5x}{-2} - \frac{6}{-2}$$

$$y = \frac{5}{2}x + 3$$

6. A horizontal line and a vertical line both pass through the point $(-2, 4)$.

a) Sketch the lines.

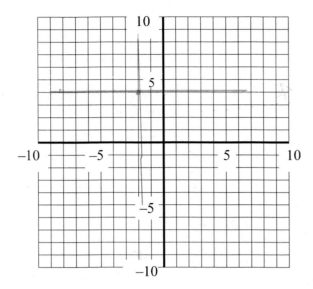

b) Write the equation of both lines.

$y = 0$
$x = $ undefined

Lesson 7   THE EQUATION OF A LINE GIVEN UNIQUE CHARACTERISTICS

In the previous lesson, a method was given for writing equations of lines when the slope and *y*-intercept are known. Now, a method will be developed in which the slope and any point on the line can be used to produce the equation of a line.

This method makes use of the slope formula:

$$m = \frac{y_2 - y_1}{x_2 - x_1}$$

Example 1

In standard from, write the equation of a line that has a slope of $\frac{3}{4}$ and passes through the point (–2, 5).

Solution

Step 1

List the known information:

$$m = \frac{3}{4}$$

1st point: (–2, 5)
2nd point: (*x, y*)

The 2nd point is always (*x, y*). It represents all of the unknown points on the line.

Step 2

Substitute the known values into the slope formula:

$$m = \frac{y_2 - y_1}{x_2 - x_1}$$

$$\frac{3}{4} = \frac{y - 5}{x + 2}$$

Step 3

Simplify and leave in standard form:

$$3(x + 2) = 4(y - 5)$$
$$3x + 6 = 4y - 20$$
$$3x - 4y + 26 = 0$$

The formula $(y - y_1), = (x - x_1)$ could also be used.

$$y - 5 = \frac{3}{4}(x + 2)$$
$$3x - 4y + 26$$

Example 2

Write the equation of a line that passes through the point $(3, -1)$ and has a slope of $-\dfrac{3}{5}$.

Solution

$m = -\dfrac{3}{5}$

1st point: $(3, -1)$
2nd point: (x, y)

$m = \dfrac{y_2 - y_1}{x_2 - x_1}$

$-\dfrac{3}{5} = \dfrac{y+1}{x-3}$

$-3(x-3) = 5(y+1)$

$-3x + 9 = 5y + 5$

$-3x - 5y + 4 = 0$

$3x + 5y - 4 = 0$

In many cases, the information about the slope and the point is not given directly. Sometimes, two points are given. In this case, the slope can be calculated from the two points and then either of the points can be used to write the equation.

Example 3

Write the equation of the line that passes through the points $(3, -4)$ and $(1, 2)$.

Solution

First, determine the slope:

$m = \dfrac{y_2 - y_1}{x_2 - x_1}$

$m = \dfrac{2 + 4}{1 - 3}$

$m = -3$

Now, choose either point and write the equation:

$m = -3$

1st point: $(3, -4)$
2nd point: (x, y)

$$m = \frac{y_2 - y_1}{x_2 - x_1}$$

$$-3 = \frac{y + 4}{x - 3}$$

$$-3(x - 3) = (y + 4)$$

$$-3x + 9 = y + 4$$

$$-3x - y + 5 = 0$$

$$3x + y - 5 = 0$$

Sometimes, information about a related line, such as a parallel or perpendicular line, is given. This information must be used to find the information that is needed to write the equation.

Example 4

Write the equation of a line in standard form and in slope y-intercept form. The line has an x-intercept of -4 and is perpendicular to the line defined by the equation $y = \frac{2}{5}x + 4$.

Solution

First find the slope.

The line that is perpendicular has a slope of $\frac{2}{5}$. The negative reciprocal is the required slope of $m = -\frac{5}{2}$.

The point is the x-intercept of -4, which can be written as $(-4, 0)$.

Now, write the equation.

$$m = -\frac{5}{2}$$

1st point: $(-4, 0)$
2nd point: (x, y)

$$m = \frac{y_2 - y_1}{x_2 - x_1}$$

$$-\frac{5}{2} = \frac{y - 0}{x + 4}$$

$$-5(x + 4) = 2y$$

$$-5x - 20 = 2y$$

$$-5x - 2y - 20 = 0$$

$$5x + 2y + 20 = 0$$

Now, rearrange to slope y-intercept form.

$$5x + 2y + 20 = 20$$

$$2y = -5x - 20$$

$$y = -\frac{5}{2}x - 10$$

As long as the slope and a point can be determined from a graph, the equation of a line can be written from the graph. The best point to use is the y-intercept, but this cannot always be read exactly, in which case another point should be used.

Example 5

Write the equation of the line on the graph below in standard form.

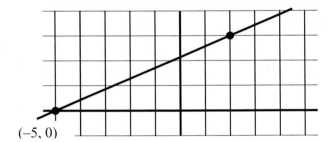

$(-5, 0)$

Solution

Since the y-intercept is not easily readable, another point will be used, such as $(2, 3)$.

Calculate the slope.

$$m = \frac{y_2 - y_1}{x_2 - x_1}$$

$$m = \frac{3 - 0}{2 + 5}$$

$$m = \frac{3}{7}$$

$m = \dfrac{3}{7}$

1st point: $(-5, 0)$

2nd point: (x, y)

$m = \dfrac{y_2 - y_1}{x_2 - x_1}$

$\dfrac{3}{7} = \dfrac{y - 0}{x + 5}$

$3(x + 5) = 7y$

$3x + 15 = 7y$

$3x - 7y + 15 = 0$

PRACTICE EXERCISES

1. Which of the following alternatives does **not** provide enough information to write the equation of a line?
    A. A point on the line and the slope of the line
    B. Two points on the line
    C. The slope and the sign of the slope
    D. The x and y-intercepts

2. The equation $2x + 3y - 13 = 0$ was written using which of the following slopes and points?
    A. $m = \dfrac{2}{3}; (1, 5)$
    B. $m = \dfrac{2}{3}; (5, 1)$
    C. $m = -\dfrac{2}{3}; (1, 5)$
    D. $m = -\dfrac{2}{3}; (5, 1)$

    $$\frac{3y}{3} = \frac{-2x}{3} + \frac{13}{3}$$
    $$y = -\frac{2}{3}x + \frac{13}{3}$$

    $$5 = -\frac{2}{3}\cdot\frac{1}{1} + \frac{13}{3}$$
    $$5 = -\frac{2}{3} + \frac{13}{3}$$

3. A line with an x-intercept of -2 that is perpendicular to the line described by the equation $y = -\dfrac{4}{7}x + 3$ has a slope of
    A. $m = -\dfrac{4}{7}$ and one point on the line is $(-2, 0)$
    B. $m = -\dfrac{4}{7}$ and one point on the line is $(0, -2)$
    C. $m = \dfrac{7}{4}$ and one point on the line is $(-2, 0)$
    D. $m = \dfrac{7}{4}$ and one point on the line is $(0, -2)$

    $$y = -\frac{4}{7}x + 3$$
    $$y = \frac{7}{4}x + 3$$
    $$0 = \frac{7}{4}(-\frac{2}{1}) + 3$$
    $$-\frac{7}{2} + \frac{3}{1}$$
    $$-\frac{7}{2} + \frac{6}{2} = -\frac{1}{2}$$
    $$-7 + 6$$

4. Write the equations of the following lines in standard form and in slope y-intercept form.

    a) A line that passes through the point (7, 10) and has a slope of $-\dfrac{4}{3}$.

    b) A line that passes through the points (2, 6) and (–1, 1).

    b) A line that is parallel to the line described by the equation $2x - 9y + 18 = 0$ and that passes through the point (–3, 5).

    d)

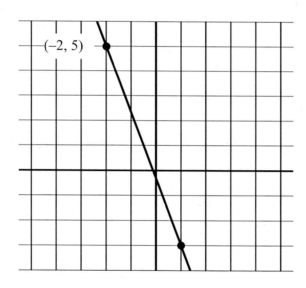

REVIEW SUMMARY

In this unit, you have learned how to . . .

- graph linear and non-linear data, using appropriate scales

- solve problems involving distances between points on a coordinate plane, using the distance formula as required

$$d = \sqrt{(x_2 - x_1)^2 + (y_2 - y_1)^2}$$

- solve problems involving the midpoints of line segments, using the midpoint formula as required

$$M = \left(\frac{x_1 + x_2}{2}, \frac{y_1 + y_2}{2} \right)$$

- solve problems involving rise, run, and slope of line segments, using the slope formula as required

$$m = \frac{y_2 - y_1}{x_2 - x_1} \qquad = \frac{\text{rise}}{\text{run}}$$

- solve problems by using slopes of parallel and perpendicular lines and applying the knowledge that parallel lines have equal slopes and perpendicular lines have slopes that are negative reciprocals

- determine the equation of a line given the required information including the slope and a point or two points

PRACTICE TEST

1. Which of the following situations describes a discrete relationship?

   A. The distance travelled increases as time passes.
   B. The temperature of water gradually increases over time.
   C. Each cupcake costs $1.75.
   D. A rock's height off the ground changes as time passes.

2. What is the equation of the following line?

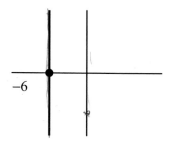

   -6

   A. $x = -6$
   B. $y = -6$
   C. $y = -6x$
   D. $x = -6y$

3. A line that is going downward from left to right has a slope that is

   A. 0
   B. undefined
   C. negative
   D. positive

Use the following diagram to answer the next question.

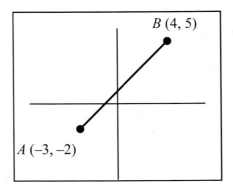

4. **a)** Find the length of *AB*. Leave the result as a reduced radical.

   b) Find the slope of *AB*.

   c) Find the midpoint of *AB*.

5. Are points $A(-3,1)$, $B(-1,6)$, and $C(3,16)$ collinear?

6. Line segment AB has a midpoint at (5, 2). If one endpoint is at $A(-3,-1)$, what is the other endpoint?

7. Triangle ABC has vertices at $A(1,6)$, $B(-4,-2)$, and $C(6,-2)$. The triangle is

    A. obtuse

    B. scalene

    C. isosceles

    D. equilateral

8. What is the equation of a line that has a slope of $\frac{3}{4}$ and a y-intercept of -7?

    A. $y = -7x + \frac{3}{4}$

    B. $y = 7x + \frac{3}{4}$

    C. $y = \frac{3}{4}x - 7$

    D. $y = \frac{3}{4}x + 7$

9. Write the equation, in standard form, that describes each of the following lines.

a) A line that passes through the point (–4, 6) and has a slope of $\frac{2}{7}$.

b) A line that passes through the points (–5, 2) and (3, 1).

c) A line that is perpendicular to $3x - 5y + 10 = 0$ and passes through the point (–6, 0).

d)

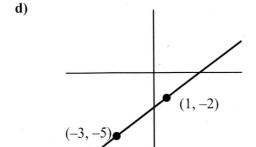

(1, –2)

(–3, –5)

FUNCTIONS AND RELATIONS

When you are finished this unit, you should be able to . . .

- represent real-life data as a function
- draw graphs of functions from their equations
- describe functions as ordered pairs, mapping diagrams, words, equations, and graphs
- use function notation to evaluate and represent functions
- determine the domain and range of a relation
- determine the intercepts and slope of a linear function
- use direct and partial variation to solve problems

Lesson	Page	Completed on
1. Function Models of Real-Life Situations	296	
2. Functions	303	
3. Domain and Range	314	
Practice Quiz	321	
4. Linear Functions	324	
5. Direct and Partial Variation	334	
Review Summary	343	
Practice Test	344	
Answers and Solutions	at the back of the book	

PREREQUISITE SKILLS AND KNOWLEDGE

Prior to beginning this unit, you should be able to . . .

- graph linear functions
- write the equations of lines
- substitute values into equations and evaluate
- solve single-variable equations

Lesson 1 FUNCTION MODELS OF REAL-LIFE SITUATIONS

There are many quantities encountered in real life that can be represented on a graph. In particular, we will be examining cases where one variable is responding to, or is a function of, the other variable.

With such relationships, key points and changes in the relationship are made clear by representing them on a graph.

Consider the following graph, which illustrates height (h) in metres as a function of time for an elevator in a five-storey building. Assume that each storey is 4 m high.

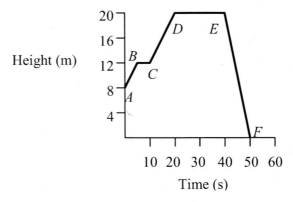

At point A on the graph, the elevator is on the third floor (the ground floor is at 0 m, the second floor is at 4 m). It then goes up at a steady speed to the fourth floor. It stays there for a few seconds, as shown from point B to C. The elevator then continues up to the sixth floor at a steady speed.
It stays at the sixth floor for several seconds, as shown from D to E, before descending non-stop at a steady speed to the ground floor.

An important thing to notice on the graph is the slope of the line segments. The greater the slope, the greater the rate of change in quantities.
In this case, slope is a measure of the velocity of the elevator.

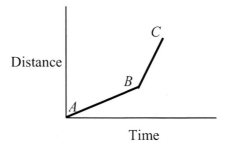

The velocity from A to B is less than the velocity from B to C.

In the graph below, the velocity is decreasing.

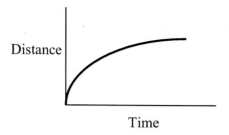

Here, the velocity is increasing.

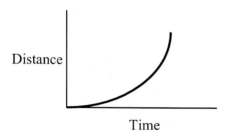

Horizontal line segments occur when the value on the vertical axis is not changing.

Example 1

The following graph shows the distance from Stephen's home as a function of time during a walk that he took to the corner store and back home.

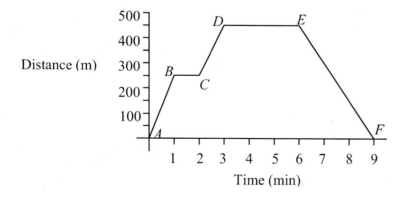

a) Stephen met a friend along the way and stopped to talk for a minute. Where is this shown on the graph?

b) What was happening from D to E?

c) Was Stephen walking faster on the way to the store or on the way back?

NOTES

Solution

a) Between *B* and *C*.

b) This is probably the time spent at the corner store.

c) The slopes from *A* to *B* and from *C* to *D* are steeper than the slope from *E* to *F*, so he was walking faster on the way to the store.

Example 2

David is driving straight down main street. When he starts, he is in a school zone. At the end of the school zone, David has to stop for a red light for a few seconds. He then drives again, but this time at a faster speed. He then reaches his destination after 4 min and stops and parks.

Sketch a graph of David's trip with distance as a function of time.

Solution

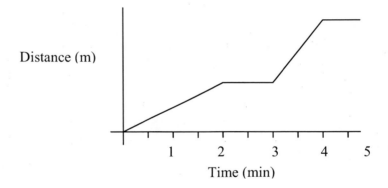

Notice that the distance does not have a scale as there was not enough information given in the question regarding the distance travelled.

Example 3

The following graph shows hours of daylight as a function of the calendar date.

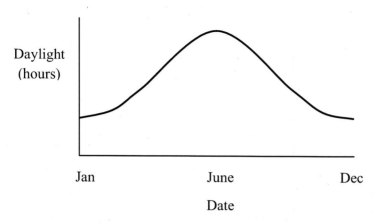

a) What month has the most hours of daylight?

b) What hemisphere does this graph represent?

Solution

a) June has the most hours of daylight.

b) This graph represents the number of hours of daylight in a location in the Northern hemisphere. If it represented the Southern hemisphere, it would have the longest day in December.

PRACTICE EXERCISES

1. Which of the following graphs of velocity as a function of time models a roller-coaster slowly climbing up one side of a hill and quickly going down the other side?

    A.

    Velocity

    Time

    B.

    Velocity

    Time

    C.

    Velocity

    Time

    D.

    Velocity

    Time

2. Below is a graph of temperature versus time. Water that was at room temperature was heated at a steady rate until it boiled.

    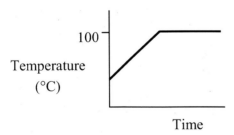

    The reason that the graph becomes horizontal is that the

    A. heat was turned off after a certain length of time

    B. water eventually evaporated and stopped heating

    C. water is continually heated, but the energy is being used to evaporate the water instead of raising its temperature

    D water boiled over and out of the pot

---

3. A hot-air balloon takes off and slowly and steadily rises to its initial altitude. The pilot maintains this altitude for several minutes and then quickly goes up a bit more. After a few more minutes, the pilot brings the balloon down slowly, almost to the ground. A few minutes later, he quickly lowers the balloon the rest of the way.

Sketch the graph of height versus time.

4. A scientist developed an alertness scale for measuring the alertness of cats. The following is a graph of alertness versus time for a particular cat that was observed over a period of 90 min.

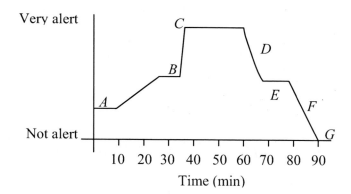

a) At what point on the graph was the cat startled by a dog barking?

b) What three consecutive letters show the cat lying down, getting very sleepy, and falling asleep?

c) What might be happening at *B*?

5. Sketch a graph of height as a function of time for yourself from birth to age 20.

Lesson 2 FUNCTIONS

Various graphs that are encountered represent relations between varying quantities. A particular type of relation in which every input has only one output is called a function. If the input has more than one output for a given input, it is described only as a relation.

Functions are such an important type of mathematical relation that there is a specific type of notation that can be used to represent them.

The "input" is the independent variable (x) and the "output" is the dependent variable (y).

Instead of writing:
$y = 2x - 3$

In function notation, it is written as:
$f(x) = 2x - 3$

Writing $f(x)$ allows the variable that is used in the function to be a part of the function's "name."

$f(x)$ is spoken as "f of x" or "f at x." It emphasizes the fact that the function is produced using x.

Another benefit of this notation is the ease with which substitution can be communicated.

With regular notation:
If $y = 2x - 3$, what is the value of y when $x = 5$?

With function notation:
If $f(x) = 2x - 3$, what is $f(5)$. In other words, if 5 is the input, what is the output?

Example 1

Given the function $f(x) = 2x - 3$, find

a) $f(5)$

b) $f(5a)$

c) $f(2\sqrt{3})$

d) $f(a - 6)$

Solution

a) $f(x) = 2x - 3$

$f(5) = 2(5) - 3$

$f(5) = 7$

b) $f(x) = 2x - 3$

$f(5a) = 2(5a) - 3$

$f(5a) = 10a - 3$

c) $f(x) = 2x - 3$

$f(2\sqrt{3}) = 2(2\sqrt{3}) - 3$

$f(2\sqrt{3}) = 4\sqrt{3} - 3$

d) $f(x) = 2x - 3$

$f(a - 6) = 2(a - 6) - 3$

$f(a - 6) = 2a - 15$

While f is the most common function, any letter can be used. Often g and h are used to represent generic functions. Sometimes, the letter is selected for its connection to the question. For example, if the question has cost represented as a function of the number of items sold, $C(n)$ might be used. To represent height as a function of time, $h(t)$ could be used.

Function notation can also be used in cases where the value of the function is known, but not the value of the input variable.

Example 2

$g(x) = 6x - 4$

Find x when $g(x) = 8$. In other words, find the input, x, if the output is 8.

> *Solution*
> $g(x) = 6x - 4$
> $8 = 6x - 4$
> $x = 2$

In cases where the substitutions are more complex, care should be taken when expanding or evaluating.

Example 3

$h(x) = x^2 - x + 3$

Find $h(a - 5)$

> *Solution*
> $h(x) = x^2 - x + 3$
> $h(a-5) = (a-5)^2 - (a-5) + 3$
> $h(a-5) = a^2 - 10a + 25 - a + 5 + 3$
> $h(a-5) = a^2 - 11a + 33$

Function notation can be used to discuss values and points on graphs as well.

NOTES

Example 4

Below is the graph of a function, $f(x)$.

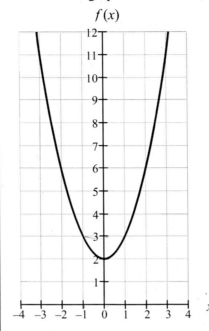

Find the following values:–4

a) $f(-1)$

b) $f(2)$

c) x when $f(x) = 11$

Solution

a) $f(-1) = 3$

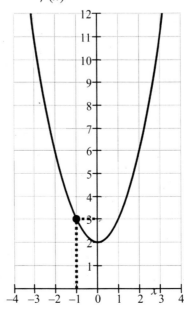

b) $f(2) = 6$

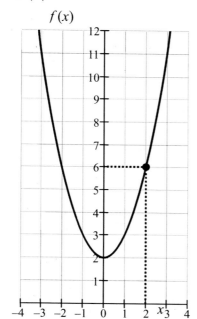

c) $x = 3$

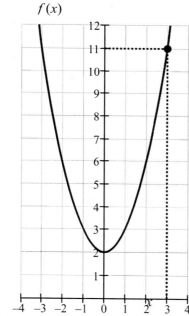

In addition to being written in the form of an equation, functions can be expressed as words, ordered pairs, tables of value, mapping diagrams, and graphs. Regardless of the form in which a function is expressed, it still must have a single output for each input.

Example 5

State whether or not each of the following relations is a function.

a) $y = 4x^2$

b) 3 times a number minus 5

c)

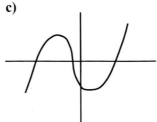

d)

x	y
1	10
1	20
2	40
3	50

e)

-2	$\rightarrow$	1
1	$\rightarrow$	4
2	$\rightarrow$	1
3	$\rightarrow$	-4

Solution.

a) Yes. Each value substituted in for x will have a single output y.

b) Yes. Every value that is multiplied by 3 and has 5 subtracted from it will have only one resulting value.

c) Yes. Each value on the horizontal axis produces only one point on the graph. The graph passes the vertical line test.

d) No. The input value of 1 has two separate outputs, 10 and 20, so it is a relation.

e) Yes.

It is important to be able to move between the different forms of a function. One of the most common translations is from an equation to a table of values.

Example 6

Express the function $h(t) = t^2 + 4$ as a table of values and as a graph.

Solution

Using the graphing calculator:

Enter the equation into the "$y =$" display and use $\boxed{\text{TABLE}}$ to find the coordinates. Often, the x-value of $-2, 1, 0, 1, 2$ are used, but any x-values could be chosen.

Display the table:

t	$h\,(t)$
-2	8
-1	5
0	4
1	5
2	8

Display the graph.
Sketch the graph:

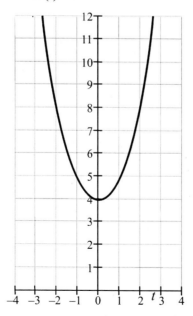

Example 7

The following function is written in words. Write it as an equation and as a table of values.

"Two less than five times a number."

Solution

Equation $f(x) = 5x - 2$

Table of values:

The table can either be produced by entering *x*-values into the function and calculating the output, or it can be produced using the graphing calculator as described in Example 6.

x	$f(x)$
–2	–12
–1	–7
0	–2
1	3
2	8

PRACTICE EXERCISES

1. Which of the following statements about functions is **not** true?

   A. They have a single output for each input.
   B. They include any expression relating two variables.
   C. The can be expressed in words, equations, ordered pairs, tables of value, and graphs.
   D. The equations can be written using $f(x)$ notation.

2. If $g(x) = 2x - 7$, then what is $g(5)$?

   A. -4
   B. 0
   C. 3
   D. 6

3. Given $f(x) = x^2 - 2x + 5$, find the value of

   a) $f(-2)$

   $$f(-2) = -2^2 - 2(-2) + 5$$
   $$4 + 4 + 5$$
   $$13$$

   b) $f(7a)$

   $$f(7a) = 7a^2 - 2(7a) + 5$$
   $$7a^2 - 14a^2 + 5$$
   $$\frac{-7a^2 + 5}{49a^2 - 14a^2 + 5}$$

   c) $f(\sqrt{3})$

   d) $f(s+3)$

   $$f(s+3) = (s+3)^2 - 2(s+3) + 5$$
   $$s^2 + 9$$

4. If $C(n) = 1.25n + 2.50$, what is n when $C(n) = 7.50$?

$$7.50 = 1.25n + 2.50$$

$$\frac{5.0}{1.25} = \frac{1.25n}{1.25}$$

5. Use the graph below to find the following values.

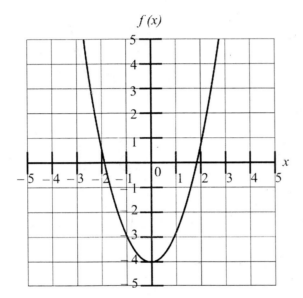

a) $f(-3)$

b) $f(0)$

c) $f(2)$

d) Find x when $f(x) = -3$.

6. Which of the following relations is **not** a function?

A.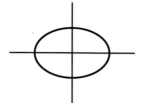

B. $y = 2x - 10$

C.

x	y
1	0
2	4
3	8

D. A number is squared and increased by 10.

7. Express the following function in words and as an equation.

x	$g(x)$
0	0
1	6
2	12
3	18

Lesson 3   DOMAIN AND RANGE

NOTES

Two of the important defining characteristics of a relation are the domain and range of the relation.

Domain: The set of all first, or input, values, often represented by the variable *x*.

Range: The set of all second, or output, values, often represented by the variable *y*.

On graphs, the domain is found along the *x*-axis and the range is found along the *y*-axis.

Sometimes, the values contained in the domain and range can be stated in the form of a list. At other times, it is impossible to list all values, and it is helpful to us the inequality symbols

\> greater than
≥ greater than or equal to
< less than
≥ less than or equal to

Example 1

State the domain and range for the graph below.

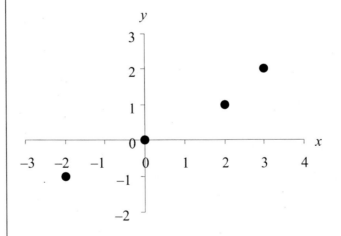

Solution

Domain: The *x*-values include the four points −2, 0, 2, 3.
Range: The *y*-values are −1, 0, 1, 2.

There are few points on the graph, and so listing the values in the domain and range is reasonable. This is not always the case.

Example 2

State the domain and range for the following graph.

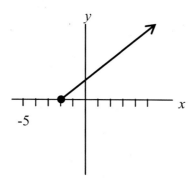

Solution

Domain: The *x*-values start at –2 and increase forever.
This can be written as $x \geq 2$ (*x* is greater than or equal to 2).

Range: The *y*-values start at 0 and increase forever. This can
be written as $y \geq 0$ (*y* is greater than or equal to 0).

Sometimes, the domain and range include all real numbers.
The way of writing this with symbols is:

$x \in \mathbb{R}$ *x* is an element of the real numbers

$y \in \mathbb{R}$ *y* is an element of the real numbers

Example 3

State the domain and range of the following function.

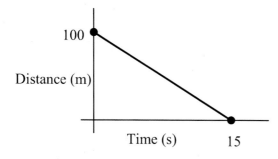

Since this example is modelling a real-life situation involving time
and distance, it is important to leave out the negative values that
occur if the graph is extended beyond the axes.

Solution

Domain: Time goes from 0 to 15 seconds, $0 \leq t \leq 15$ (*t* is
greater than or equal to 0 and less than or equal to 15).
Range: Distance goes from 0 to 100 m, $0 \leq d \leq 100$ (*d* is
greater than or equal to 0 and less than or equal to 100).

In cases where only the equation of the function is given and not the graph, it is helpful to graph the function, either by hand or on a graphing calculator, in order to determine the function's domain and range.

Example 4

State the domain and range of the following function.

$f(x) = x^2 - 3$

Solution

Since the graph was not provided and the function is not linear, the function should be graphed on a graphing calculator.

Use $X[-10, 10, 1] Y[-10, 10, 1]$ for the calculator window setting or zoom 6:standard.

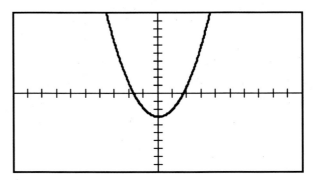

In order to state the range, it is necessary to know the value of the lowest point on the graph. This can be found using the graphing calculator's "Trace" or "Calculate Minimum" functions.

In this case, the minimum value is –3.

Domain: $x \in \mathbb{R}$
Range: $y \geq -3$

Sometimes, the values in the domain and range are discrete. Stating the number set that the values are a part of can indicate this.

Example 5

State the domain and range of the function below.

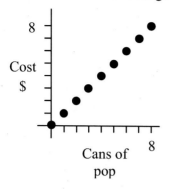

Solution

Domain: $0 \le p \le 8$; $p \in Z$ (p is an integer)

Range: $0 \le C \le 8$; $C \in Z$ (C is an integer)

When the equation of a function describes a real-life situation, it is important to take the real-life elements of the question into account.

Example 6

A ball is thrown up in the air and hits the ground 2.3 s later. The height of the ball as a function of time is described by the equation $h = -4.9t^2 + 10t + 3$.

a) Sketch a graph of the function. Use your graphing calculator to assist you.

b) State the domain and range of the function.

Solution

Notice that only positive values are included for time and height, even though a graph of the function could extend into other quadrants.

This is because both time and height cannot be negative.

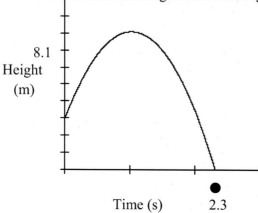

Using a calculator, determine the maximum height: 8.1 m.

Domain: $0 \le t \le 2.3$
Range: $0 \le h \le 8.1$

PRACTICE EXERCISES

1. What is the domain of the following relation?

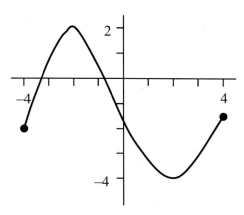

    A. $x \in \mathbb{R}$
    B. $x \geq -4$
    C. $x \leq 4$
    D. $-4 \leq x \leq 4$

2. What is the range of the function $y = x^2 + 5$?

    A. $y \geq 0$
    B. $y \in \mathbb{R}$
    C. $y \geq 5$
    D. $x \geq -5$

3. For each of the following relations, state the domain and range.

    a)   b)   c)

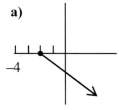   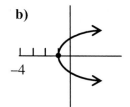   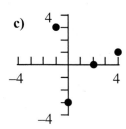

d) $y = 2x + 3$

e) $y = \sqrt{x}$

f) $y = -x^2 + 6$

4. Stephen is walking home from the gym. His distance (d) from home in blocks as a function of time (t) in minutes is given by the following equation:

$d = -2t + 10$

a) Sketch the graph of the function.

b) Give the domain and range of the function.

PRACTICE QUIZ

1. The following graph represents distance versus time.

Distance

Time

Which line segment represents the greatest speed?

A. *A* to *B*
B. *B* to *C*
C. *C* to *D*
D. *D* to *E*

2. Which of the following relations has a domain that is $x \in R$?

A. 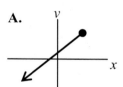   **B.** 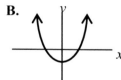   **C.** 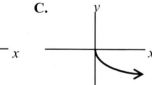   **D.**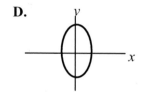

3. a) What is a function? _____

_____

b) Name three ways that functions can be expressed.

4. If $C(n) = 1.5n + 30$, what is the value of

   a) $C(26)$?

   b) n, when $C(n) = 60$?

5. If $f(x) = 2x^2 + x$, what is the value of

   a) $f(a-3)$?

   b) $f(3\sqrt{6})$?

6. State the domain and range of the following relations.

   a)

   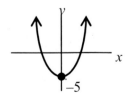

   b)

   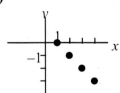

7. A particular function is defined by the equation $f(x) = -4x + 5$.

    a) Complete the following table of values.

x	$f(x)$
-1	
0	
1	

    b) Sketch the graph.

Lesson 4 LINEAR FUNCTIONS

The focus of this lesson will be on linear functions. In particular, the meaning of important characteristics of linear functions such as

Intercepts
Slope
Domain
Range

Intercepts have already been discussed but will now be dealt with in more detail.

x-intercept: point where the graph crosses the x-axis (therefore, $y = 0$)
y-intercept: point where the graph crosses the y-axis (therefore, $x = 0$)

In the following graph, point *A* is the x-intercept and point *B* is the y-intercept.

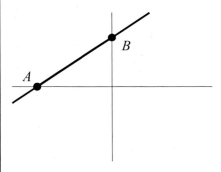

It is useful to note that x-intercepts can always be expressed as an ordered pair in the form $(x, 0)$ and y-intercepts can be expressed in the form $(0, y)$.

This information is useful because it enables the intercepts to be determined without the graph as long as the equation of the function is known.

Example 1

Determine the x-and y-intercepts of the following function, and use them to sketch the graph.

$2x - 3y = 12$

Solution

x-intercept:

Since the x-intercept is the point $(x, 0)$, 0 can be substituted into the equation. The equation can then be solved to find the value of x.

$$2x - 3y = 12$$
$$2x - 3(0) = 12$$
$$2x = 12$$
$$x = 6$$

The x-intercept is at 6, or $(6, 0)$.

y-intercept:
Using $(0, y)$:

$$2x - 3y = 12$$
$$2(0) - 3y = 12$$
$$-3y = 12$$
$$y = -4$$

The y-intercept is at –4, or $(0, -4)$.

Sketch the graph:

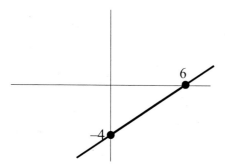

Linear functions that model real-life situations have intercepts that have important significance in the context of the question. Often, variables other than x and y are used, so the intercepts may not be called x-intercepts and y-intercepts.

Example 2

The distance from Lexi's home to Amorita's home is approximately 400 km. Lexi drives to Amorita's house at a speed of 100 km/h.

The distance (d) in kilometres remaining on her drive as a function of time (t) in hours is described by the equation

$$d = -100t + 400$$

a) Determine the intercepts.
b) Sketch a graph of the function.
c) Describe the significance of the intercepts.

Solution

a) t-intercept: $(t, 0)$

$$0 = -100t + 400$$

$$t = 4$$

d-intercept: $(0, d)$

$$d = -100(0) + 400$$

$$d = 400$$

Graph:

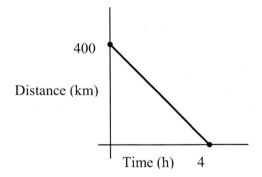

c) The d-intercept represents the start of the trip, where no time has passed and 400 km of distance remain.

The t-intercept represents the end of the trip, where Lexi has driven 4 h and no distance remains.

The slope is also an important characteristic of a linear function. It describes the rate that the output (responding) variable is changing with respect to the input variable. Some rates that the slope commonly represents are

Speed/Velocity (distance versus time)
Rate of pay (earning versus time)
Cost per item (cost versus number of items)

The slope can always be determined from a graph or table of values by using two points and the slope formula. The slope can also be determined when given the equation of a function by arranging the equation into the $y = mx + b$ form.

Example 3

The following table of values represents David's earnings as a function of the number of hours he worked.

Hours	Earnings
2	$15.90
4	$31.80
6	$47.70
8	$63.60

a) Determine the slope of the function.
b) What does the slope represent?

To interpret the slope, it is helpful to look at the units:

$$m = \frac{\text{rise}}{\text{run}} = \frac{\$}{h}$$

Solution

a) Use two points and the slope formula.
(2, 15.9) and (4, 31.8)

$$m = \frac{y_2 - y_1}{x_2 - x_1}$$

$$m = \frac{31.8 - 15.9}{4 - 2}$$

$$m = 7.95$$

b) The slope represents David's rate of pay, which is $7.95/hour.

Example 4

The following graph represents the distance (*d*) in metres of Stephen's remote-control car from him as a function of time (*t*) in seconds.

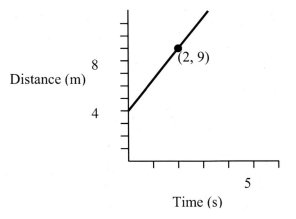

a) Determine the slope.

b) What does the slope represent?

Decimals are often more meaningful in real–life scenarios than fractions.

Solution

a)

$$m = \frac{y_2 - y_1}{x_2 - x_1}$$

$$m = \frac{9 - 4}{2 - 0}$$

$$m = \frac{5}{2}$$

$$m = 2.5$$

b) The slope represents the speed of the car, which is 2.5 m/s.

Discussing a function in terms of all of its characteristics gives a clear understanding of the function and its meaning.

    328

Example 5

Amorita is travelling away from home for 5 h. The following function expresses her distance (d) from home in kilometres as a function of time (t) in hours.

$$d = 80t + 40$$

a) Determine the intercepts.
b) Sketch the graph.
c) What does the d-intercept represent?
d) Determine the slope.
e) What does the slope represent?
f) Determine the domain and range of the function.
g) Is the function continuous or discrete?

Solution.

a) t-intercept $(t, 0)$

$$d = 80t + 40$$

$$0 = 80t + 40$$

$$t = -\frac{40}{80}$$

$$t = -0.5$$

d-intercept

$$d = 80(0) + 40$$

$$d = 40$$

b)

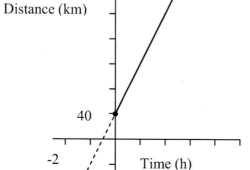

The dotted line represents information that is helpful for drawing the graph but has no real meaning in the real-life situation.

c) The *d*-intercept of 40 km represents how far Amorita is from home when her trip starts.

d) From the equation $d = 80t + 40$, we know that the slope is 80.

e) The slope represents a speed of 80 km/h.

f) The trip starts at (0, 40) and ends at (5, 440).
Domain: $0 \le t \le 5$
Range: $40 \le d \le 440$

g) The function is continuous.

PRACTICE EXERCISES

1. The *x*-intercept of the following linear function is

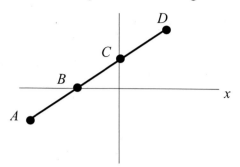

   A. *A*
   B. *B*
   C. *C*
   D. *D*

2. A particular linear function represents distance as a function of time. The slope of the function represents

   A. distance
   B. time
   C. speed
   D. acceleration

3. Determine the *x*- and *y*- intercepts of the following linear functions.
   a) $4x - 7y = 56$ **b)** $5x - 4y + 25 = 0$

$$\frac{4x}{4} = \frac{56 + 7y}{4}$$

$$x = 14 + \frac{7}{4}y$$

4. **a)** Determine the slope of the following function and describe what it represents.

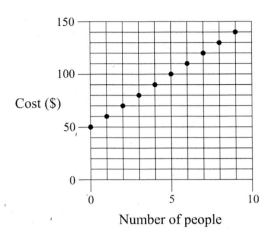

Number of people

b) Is the function continuous or discrete?

5. A gas tank contains 45 L of fuel. The car has a fuel consumption rating of 9 L/100 km. The following graph shows the fuel in the tank as a function of the distance driven.

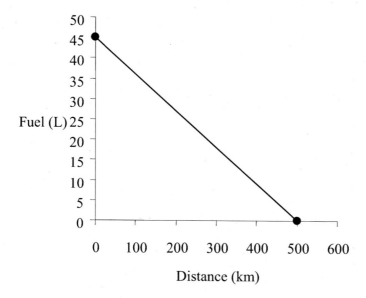

a) Determine the intercepts.

b) What do the intercepts represent?

c) Determine the slope.

d) What does the slope represent?

e) Determine the domain and range.

Lesson 5 DIRECT AND PARTIAL VARIATION

Two types of linear functions that model real-life situations are called **direct variation** and **partial variation**.

DIRECT VARIATION

With direct variation relations, the output or responding variable is determined by multiplying the input or manipulated variable by a constant amount. This constant amount is called the constant of variation.
The constant of variation is equal to the slope of the graph of the function.

Like all linear functions, direct variations can be in the form of equations, tables of value, graphs, or words.

Direct variation graphs have a y-intercept of 0, and so the equations take the form $y = mx + 0$, or $y = mx$.

The graphs take the following forms:

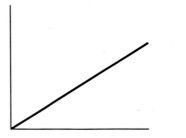 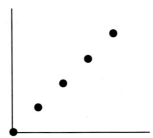

Continuous Direct Variation   Discrete Direct Variation

The constant of variation is sometimes represented by k instead of m.

The phrase "y varies directly as x" is written as the equation $y = mx$, where x is the constant of variation.

Example 1

The amount of commission (c) earned varies directly with the value of clothing sold (s).

If $500 worth of clothing is sold, $25 in commission is earned.

a) Determine the constant of variation.

b) Write the equation representing the commission earned as a function of clothing sold.

c) Determine the commission that would be made on $1 600 worth of sales.

d) How many dollars worth of sales are required to earn $115 in commission?

e) Graph the function.

Solution

a) Since c varies directly with s, the equation is in the form $c = ms$.

To find m, substitute the values for $c = 25$ and $s = 500$.

$$c = ms$$
$$25 = m(500)$$
$$m = \frac{25}{500}$$
$$m = 0.05$$

b) To write the equation, the determined constant of variation can be substituted into the formula.

$$c = ms$$
$$c = 0.05s$$

c) When $s = 1\ 600$:

$$c = 0.05s$$
$$c = 0.05(1\ 600)$$
$$c = 80$$

$80 in commission would be earned.

d) When $c = 115$:
$$c = 0.05s$$
$$115 = 0.05s$$
$$s = 2\ 300$$

There would have to be $2 300 in sales to earn $115 in commission.

e)

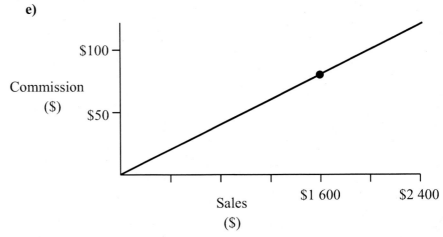

Example 2

Distance (d), in metres varies directly with respect to time (t), in seconds. When the time equals 15 s, the distance equals 18.75 m.

a) Determine the constant of variation.
b) Write the equation of the function.

Solution

a) $d = mt$
$$18.75 = m(15)$$
$$m = 1.25$$
The constant of variation is 1.25.

b) The equation of the function is
$$d = mt$$
$$d = 1.25t$$

Example 3

The following graph represents distance (*d*) as a function of time (*t*).
Write the equation of the function.

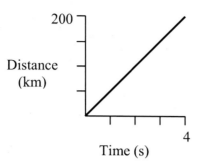

Time (s)

Solution

Since the *y*-intercept is 0, the function demonstrates direct variation.

Distance varies directly with respect to time.

$d = mt$

Using the point (4, 200):

$$d = mt$$
$$200 = m(4)$$
$$m = 50$$

The equation is $d = 50t$.

PARTIAL VARIATION

Partial variation, like direct variation, has a constant that is multiplied by the input. Unlike direct variation, there is also a constant being added to this product.

Partial variations have equations in the form (also known as the slope *y*-intercept form) $y = mx + b$, where $b \neq 0$.

The graphs take the following forms:

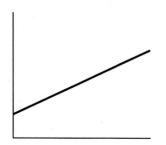 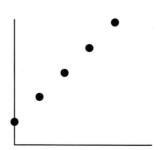

Example 4

A banquet hall rental costs $75 as a basic fee, plus $8.50 per person.

a) Complete the table of values.

Number of people	0	10	20	30	40	50
Cost ($)						

b) Write the equation with the cost of the rental as a function of the number of people.

c) Sketch a graph of the function.

d) Use the graph to estimate the cost of having a banquet with 35 people. Use the equation to check your guess.

e) Explain the significance of the y-intercept.

Solution

a)

Number of people	0	10	20	30	40	50
Cost ($)	75	160	245	330	415	500

b) $y = mx + b$

$c = mn + b$

Some students will recognize 8.50 as the rate of change, slope, or constant of variation.

Another way of finding it is by using any two points from the graph, along with the slope formula.

Use the points $(0, 75)$ and $(10, 160)$:

$$m = \frac{y_2 - y_1}{x_2 - x_1}$$

$$m = \frac{160 - 75}{10 - 0}$$

$$m = 8.5$$

The y-intercept is the point in the form $(0, y)$. In this case, it is $(0, 75)$. So, $b = 75$.

$$c = mn + b$$

$$c = 8.5n + 75$$

c)

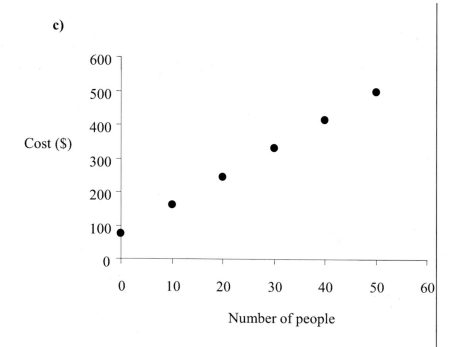

d)

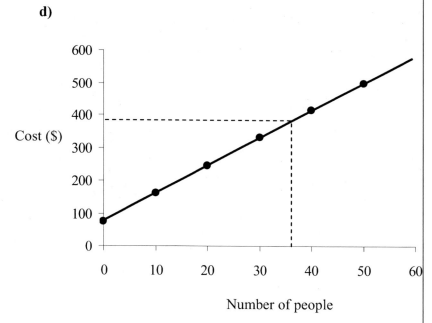

Using the equation:

$$c = 8.5n + 75$$
$$c = 8.5(35) + 75$$
$$c = 372$$

e) The y-intercept, \$75, is the fixed basic rental fee.

PRACTICE EXERCISES

1. Which of the following graphs represents a discrete partial variation?

A.

B.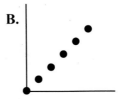

C.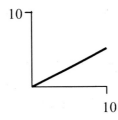

D.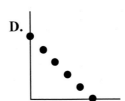

2. The following graph presents a

A. direct variation with a constant of variation that is less than 1
B. direct variation with a constant of variation that is greater than 1
C. partial variation with a constant of variation that is less than 1
D. partial variation with a constant of variation that is less than 1

3. The cost of a phone bill varies directly with respect to the number of minutes talked. When the number of minutes equals 236, the phone bill is $16.52.

a) Determine the constant of variation.

b) Write the equation of the function.

4. The following graph represents the depth (*h*) in centimetres of the water in a bathtub as a function of time (*t*) in seconds.

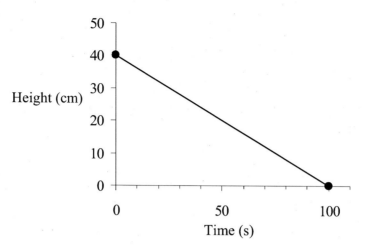

Height (cm)

Time (s)

a) What type of variation does the graph represent?

b) Write the equation of the function.

c) Using the graph, estimate the water depth after 65s. Check your estimate with the equation.

d) Describe what is happening in this situation.

e) What does the *h*-intercept represent?

f) State the domain and range of the function.

5. The number of centimetres of snow (*s*) on the ground varies directly with the time (*t*) in hours that the snow falls. After 5 hours, there are 6 cm of snow on the ground.

a) Find the constant of variation.

b) Write the equation of the function.

c) Sketch a graph of the function.

d) What is the significance of the slope of the graph?

e) If the snow continues to fall for 2 full days, how much will be on the ground?

REVIEW SUMMARY

In this unit, you have learned how to . . .

- represent real-life data as a function

- draw graphs of functions from their equations by hand and using technology

- describe functions as ordered pairs, mapping diagrams, words, equations, and graphs that change from one form to another

- use function notation to evaluate and represent functions, using functions such as $f(x)$

- determine the domain and range of a relation

- determine the intercepts and slope of a linear function

- use direct and partial variation to solve problems with the formulas

$$y = mx \quad \text{and} \quad y = mx + b$$

PRACTICE TEST

1. Which of the following graphs is **not** a function?

    A.
    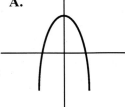

    B.
    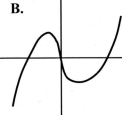

    C.
    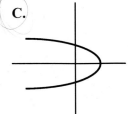

    D.
    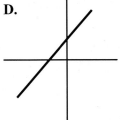

2. What is the domain and range of the following relation?

    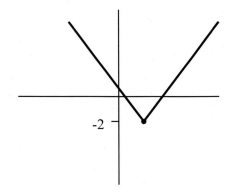

    A. Domain: $x \in \mathbb{R}$
        Range: $y \geq -2$

    B. Domain: $x \in \mathbb{R}$
        Range: $y \leq -2$

    C. Domain: $x \geq -2$
        Range: $y \in \mathbb{R}$

    D. Domain: $x \leq -2$
        Range: $y \in \mathbb{R}$

3. Which of the following statements about partial variation is **not** true?

   A. The equation is in the form $y = mx + b$, where $b \neq 0$.
   B. The graph includes the point (0, 0).
   C. The function increases/decreases at a constant rate.
   D. It can be represented as a table of values.

4. If $f(x) = 2x^2 - 5x + 3$, then what is the value of

   a) $f(4)$?

   $$f(4) = (2)(4^2) - 5(4) + 3$$
   $$32 - 20 + 3$$
   $$20$$
   $$12 + 3$$
   $$15$$

   b) $f(-2)$?

   $$2(-2)^2 - 5(-2) + 3$$
   $$2(-4) - -10 + 3$$
   $$-8 - (-7)$$
   $$-1$$

   c) $f(4\sqrt{2})$?

   d) $f(3a)$?

   e) $f(a-3)$?

5. Which of the following graphs shows that velocity is increasing?

A.

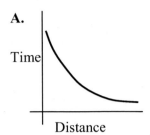

B.

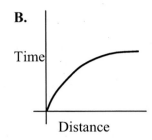

C.

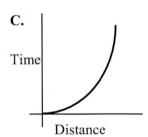

D.

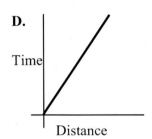

6. What are the x-and y-intercepts of the function defined by the equation $4x - 6y + 48 = 0$?

   A. x-intercept: 8
       y-intercept: 12

   B. x-intercept: 12
       y-intercept: 8

   C. x-intercept: 8
       y-intercept: -12

   D. x-intercept: -12
       y-intercept: 8

7. The following graph shows height as a function of time. Write the equation for this function.

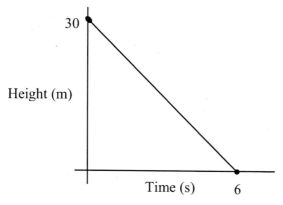

8. The following table shows cost as a function of the number of the people. Cost (*C*) varies directly with the number of people (*n*).

n	*C* ($)
10	89.50
20	179.00
30	268.50

a) Determine the equation of the function.

b) What does the constant of variation represent?

c) Is this function discrete or continuous?

NOTES

Answers

and

Solutions

CASTLE ROCK

RESEARCH CORP

NOTES

TRIGONOMETRY

Lesson 1 Sine, Cosine, and Tangent Ratios

PRACTICE EXERCISES
Answers and Solutions

1. Triangles **B**, **C**, and **D** have enough information provided to be solved, triangle **A** does not.

3. **a)** $\sin 50° = \dfrac{x}{20}$

$x = 20 \sin 50°$

$x \approx 15.3$ m

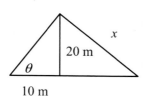

20 m

x

θ

10 m

b) $\cos 31° = \dfrac{3.1}{x}$

$x = \dfrac{3.1}{\cos 31°}$

$x \approx 3.6$ cm

5. **a)** Find $\overline{AB}$ by using the Pythagorean theorem:

$c^2 = a^2 + b^2$

$\left(\overline{AB}\right)^2 = 21^2 + 18^2$

$\overline{AB} = \sqrt{21^2 + 18^2}$

≈ 27.7 cm

Find $\angle A$ by using the tangent ratio:

$\tan A = \dfrac{18}{21}$

$A = \tan^{-1}\left(\dfrac{18}{21}\right)$

$A \approx 40.6°$

Find $\angle B$ by using the sum of the angles in a triangle:

$A + B + C = 180°$

$\tan^{-1}\left(\dfrac{18}{21}\right) + B + 90° = 180°$

$B = 180° - \left(\tan^{-1}\left(\dfrac{18}{21}\right) + 90°\right)$

$B \approx 49.4°$

b) Find $\angle A$:

$A + B + C = 180°$

$A + 36° + 90° = 180°$

$A = 180° - (36° + 90°)$

$A = 54°$

Find $\overline{AB}$ by using the sine ratio:

$\sin 36° = \dfrac{15}{\overline{AB}}$

$\overline{AB} = \dfrac{15}{\sin 36°}$

$\overline{AB} \approx 25.5$ cm

Find $\overline{BC}$ by using the tangent ratio:

$\tan 36° = \dfrac{15}{\overline{BC}}$

$\overline{BC} = \dfrac{15}{\tan 36°}$

$\overline{BC} \approx 20.6$ cm

Lesson 2 Problems Involving Two Right Triangles

PRACTICE EXERCISES
Answers and Solutions

1. C

ϕ is the angle of elevation because it is measured from the horizontal upward.

3. a) $\tan\theta = \dfrac{20}{10}$

$\theta = \tan^{-1}\left(\dfrac{20}{10}\right)$

$\theta \approx 63.4°$

$\theta + 90° + \phi = 180°$

$\phi = 180° - 90° - \tan^{-1}\left(\dfrac{20}{10}\right)$

$\phi \approx 26.6°$

$\sin\phi = \dfrac{20}{x}$

$x = \dfrac{20}{\sin 26.6°}$

$x \approx 44.7$ m

b) $\cos 42° = \dfrac{x}{45}$

$45\cos 42° = x$

$x \approx 33.4°$

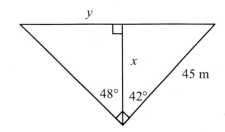

$\tan 48° = \dfrac{y}{x}$

$x\tan 48° = y$

$\left(45\cos\left(42°\right)\right)\tan 48° = y$

$y \approx 37.1$ m

5.

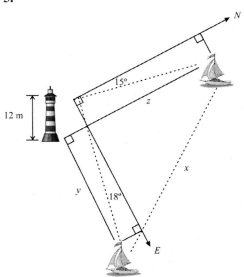

To find x, we must find y and z.

Find y:
Eastern plane

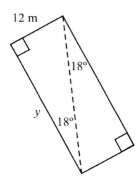

$\tan 18° = \dfrac{12}{y}$

$y = \dfrac{12}{\tan 18°}$

≈ 36.9 m

Find z:
Northern plane

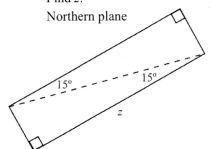

$$\tan 15° = \frac{12}{z}$$

$$z = \frac{12}{\tan 15°}$$

$$\approx 44.8 \text{ m}$$

Now, find x:
Overhead view

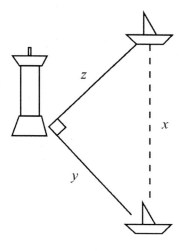

$$c^2 = a^2 + b^2$$

$$x^2 = \left(\frac{12}{\tan 15°}\right)^2 + \left(\frac{12}{\tan 18°}\right)^2$$

$$x = \sqrt{\left(\frac{12}{\tan 15°}\right)^2 + \left(\frac{12}{\tan 18°}\right)^2}$$

$$x \approx 58.0 \text{ m}$$

Lesson 3 Sine and Cosine for Angles from 0° to 180°

PRACTICE EXERCISES
Answers and Solutions

1. B

The answer is 115°, since $180° - 65° = 115°$.

3. a) $\theta = \cos^{-1}(0.5)$

$\theta = 60°$

b) $\theta = \sin^{-1}(0.5)$

$\theta = 30°$

and

$\theta = 180° - 30°$

$\theta = 150°$

c) $\theta = \cos^{-1}\left(\frac{-2}{3}\right)$

$\theta \approx 131.8°$

d) $\theta = \sin^{-1}\left(\frac{1}{3}\right)$

$\theta \approx 19.5°$

and

$\theta = 180 - 19.5°$

$\theta = 160.5°$

Practice Quiz

Answers and Solutions

1. a) θ and α

b) γ and z

3. a) $\cos\theta = 0.223\,3$

$\theta = \cos^{-1}(0.223\,3)$

$\theta \approx 77°$

b) $\sin\theta = 0.258\,9$

$\theta = \sin^{-1}(0.258\,9)$

$\theta \approx 15°$

and

$\theta = 180° - 15°$

$\theta \approx 165°$

Lesson 4 The Sine Law

PRACTICE EXERCISES
Answers and Solutions

1. a) C

$$\frac{\sin 70°}{x} = \frac{\sin 80°}{15}$$

3. a) $\dfrac{\sin 81°}{55} = \dfrac{\sin \theta}{32}$

$$\sin \theta = \frac{32 \sin 81°}{55}$$

$$\theta = \sin^{-1}\left(\frac{32 \sin 81°}{55}\right)$$

$$\theta \approx 35°$$

b) $\dfrac{\sin 40°}{34} = \dfrac{\sin \theta}{37}$

$$\sin \theta = \frac{37 \sin 40°}{34}$$

$$\theta = \sin^{-1}\left(\frac{37 \sin 40°}{34}\right)$$

$$\theta \approx 44°$$

5. First you need to know the angle at point Z.

$$\angle X + \angle Y + \angle Z = 180°$$

$$\angle Z = 180° - \angle X - \angle Y$$

$$= 180° - 100° - 50°$$

$$= 30°$$

Then, use the Sine Law:

$$\frac{\sin 30°}{25 \text{ m}} = \frac{\sin 50°}{x}$$

$$x = \frac{25 \text{ m} \times \sin 50°}{\sin 30°}$$

$$x \approx 38.3 \text{ m}$$

Therefore, the length of $\overline{XZ}$ is approximately 38.3 m.

Lesson 5 The Cosine Law

PRACTICE EXERCISES
Answers and Solutions

1. a) Cosine Law

b) Sine Law

c) Cosine Law

d) Sine Law
Note that the 3rd angle must be determined first.
$$180° - (100° + 50°) = 30°$$

3. a) $\cos A = \dfrac{b^2 + c^2 - a^2}{2bc}$

$$\cos \theta = \frac{18^2 + 12^2 - 19^2}{2(18)(12)}$$

$$\theta = \cos^{-1}\left(\frac{18^2 + 12^2 - 19^2}{2(18)(12)}\right)$$

$$\theta \approx 75.7°$$

b) $\cos A = \dfrac{b^2 + c^2 - a^2}{2bc}$

$$\cos \alpha = \frac{81^2 + 72^2 - 107^2}{2(81)(72)}$$

$$\alpha = \cos^{-1}\left(\frac{81^2 + 72^2 - 107^2}{2(81)(72)}\right)$$

$$\alpha \approx 89.4°$$

Lesson 6 Mixed Problems

PRACTICE EXERCISES
Answers and Solutions

1. a) First, determine the side labelled y below by using the tangent ratio.

$$\tan 20° = \frac{y}{14}$$
$$14 \tan 20° = y$$

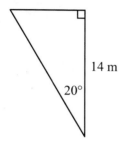

14 m

20°

Now, use the Cosine Law to find x:

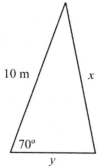

10 m

x

70º

y

$$a^2 = b^2 + c^2 - 2bc \cos A$$
$$x^2 = 10^2 + y^2 - 2(10)(y)\cos 70°$$
$$x = \sqrt{10^2 + (14\tan 20°)^2 - 2(10)(14\tan 20°)\cos 70°}$$
$$x \approx 9.5 \text{ m}$$

b) First, determine the side labelled y by using the Sine Law.

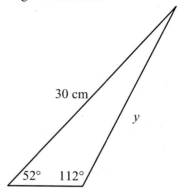

30 cm

y

52°   112°

$$\frac{\sin 112°}{30} = \frac{\sin 52°}{y}$$
$$y = \frac{30\sin 52°}{\sin 112°}$$
$$y \approx 25.5 \text{ cm}$$

Now, find x by using Sine Ratio:

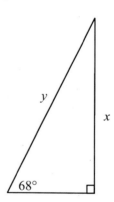

y

x

68°

$$\sin 68° = \frac{x}{y}$$
$$x = y\sin 68°$$
$$x = \left(\frac{30\sin 52°}{\sin 112°}\right)\sin 68°$$

$$x \approx 23.6 \text{ cm}$$

3. First, determine the length of the bases of the vertical triangles by using the tangent ratio.

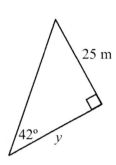

$$\tan 42° = \frac{25}{y}$$

$$y = \frac{25}{\tan 42°}$$

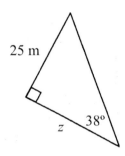

$$\tan 38° = \frac{25}{z}$$

$$z = \frac{25}{\tan 38°}$$

Now, determine x by using the Cosine Law:

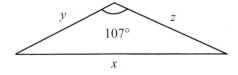

$$a^2 = b^2 + c^2 - 2bc \cos A$$
$$x^2 = y^2 + z^2 - 2(y)(z)\cos 107°$$
$$x = \sqrt{\left(\frac{25}{\tan 42°}\right)^2 + \left(\frac{25}{\tan 38°}\right)^2 - 2\left(\frac{25}{\tan 42°}\right)\left(\frac{25}{\tan 38°}\right)\cos 107°}$$
$$x \approx 41.8 \text{ m}$$

Answers and Solutions

1. D

3. a) $\sin\theta = \frac{11}{25}$

$$\theta = \sin^{-1}\left(\frac{11}{25}\right)$$

$$\theta \approx 26°$$

b) $\cos 71° = \frac{4.5}{x}$

$$x = \frac{4.5}{\cos 71°}$$

$$x \approx 13.8 \text{ cm}$$

c) $\frac{\sin 30°}{23} = \frac{\sin 85°}{x}$

$$x = \frac{23\sin 85°}{\sin 30°}$$

$$x \approx 45.8 \text{ m}$$

d) $a^2 = b^2 + c^2 - 2bc\cos A$

$$x^2 = 18^2 + 17^2 - 2(18)(17)\cos(95°)$$

$$x = \sqrt{18^2 + 17^2 - 2(18)(17)\cos(95°)}$$

$$x \approx 25.8 \text{ m}$$

e) $\cos A = \frac{b^2 + c^2 - a^2}{2bc}$

$$\cos\theta = \frac{140^2 + 130^2 - 200^2}{2(140)(130)}$$

$$\theta = \cos^{-1}\left(\frac{140^2 + 130^2 - 200^2}{2(140)(130)}\right)$$

$$\theta \approx 96°$$

f) $\tan 59° = \dfrac{x}{15}$

$x = 15\tan 59°$

$x \approx 24.96°$

$\dfrac{\sin \theta}{x} = \dfrac{\sin 21°}{9}$

$\sin \theta = \dfrac{x\sin 21°}{9}$

$\sin \theta = \dfrac{15(\tan 59°)(\sin 21°)}{9}$

$\theta = \sin^{-1}\left(\dfrac{15(\tan 59°)(\sin 21°)}{9}\right)$

$\theta \approx 84°$

POLYNOMIALS

Lesson 1 Arithmetic Sequences

PRACTICE EXERCISES
Answers and Solutions

1. a) $-42, -61, -80, -99, -118$

 b) $10.9, 13.5, 16.1, 18.7, 21.3$

 c) $-3, 1, 5, 9, 13$

3. a) $a = -10$
 $d = 9$
 $t_n = a + (n-1)d$
 $t_n = -10 + (n-1)(9)$
 $t_n = 9n - 19$
 $t_{30} = 9(30) - 19$
 $t_{30} = 251$

 b) $a = 3.5$
 $d = -1.5$
 $t_n = 3.5 + (n-1)(-1.5)$
 $t_n = -1.5n + 5$
 $t_{30} = -1.5(30) + 5$
 $t_{30} = -40$

5. a) $d = 0.15$
 $n = 5$
 $t_n = 1.8$
 $t_n = a + (n-1)d$
 $1.8 = a + (5-1)(0.15)$
 $a = 1.2$

 In the first year, the ice cream cost $1.20 per cone.

 b) $t_n = a + (n-1)d$
 $t_n = 1.2 + 8(0.15)$
 $t_n = 1.2 + 1.2$
 $t_n = 2.4$

 In the 9th year, ice-cream cones will cost $2.40.

 c) $t_n = 3.45$
 $t_n = a + (n-1)d$
 $3.45 = 1.2 + (n-1)(0.15)$
 $n = 16$

 Ice cream will cost $3.45 in the 16th year.

Lesson 2 Arithmetic Series

PRACTICE EXERCISES
Answers and Solutions

1. B

The numbers have a common difference and are being added.

3. a) $a = 2$
 $n = 6$
 $d = 3$
 $S_n = \dfrac{n}{2}[2a + (n-1)d]$
 $S_6 = \dfrac{6}{2}[2(2) + (6-1)3]$
 $S_6 = 57$

 The child will eat 57 treats over the 6 days.

 b) $71 - 57 = 14$

 14 treats will be thrown away after the 6th day.

Lesson 3 Polynomials

PRACTICE EXERCISES
Answers and Solutions

1. B

The most likely mistake would be to choose 4, as the variable x occurs twice.

3. Since there are no like terms to combine, the first binomial will contribute two terms and the first trinomial will contribute three terms. The final polynomial will have **five** terms.

5. $2(x+1)+3(x^2-2)-(x-1)$

$2x+2+3x^2-6-x+1$

$3x^2+x-3$

Lesson 4 Multiplication of Polynomials

PRACTICE EXERCISES
Answers and Solutions

1. $(2x+2)(x+3)-3(2x)$

$2x(x+3)+2(x+3)-6x$

$2x^2+6x+2x+6-6x$

$2x^2+2x+6$

3. $(x+a)^2$ $\qquad$ $(x+b)^2$

$(x+a)(x+a)$ $\qquad$ $(x+b)(x+b)$

$x(x+a)+a(x+a)$ $\qquad$ $x(x+b)+b(x+b)$

$x^2+xa+ax+a^2$ $\qquad$ $x^2+bx+bx+b^2$

$x^2+2ax+a^2$ $\qquad$ $x^2+2bx+b^2$

It was indicated that a and b were constants. This means that the numerical coefficient of the second term in each final answer is exactly twice as large as the original constant: a and $2a$.
Any answer that gives this observation, or a similar correct answer, is acceptable.

5. The volume of the larger box is found by $(x+1)^3$. The volume of the smaller cubic box is x^3.

To find the remaining space, subtract the volume of the smaller box from that of the larger box.

$(x+1)(x+1)(x+1)-x^3$

$(x^2+2x+1)(x+1)-x^3$

$x^3+3x^2+3x+1-x^3$

$3x^2+3x+1$

The equation for the larger volume is x^3+3x^2+3x+1.

$x = 1$ cm

$=3(1)^2+3(1)+1$

$=3+3+1$

$=7$ cm^3

The empty space has a volume of 7 cm^3.

Lesson 5 Factoring Polynomials

PRACTICE EXERCISES
Answers and Solutions

1. B

3. $4-3x-x^2$ multiplied by (-1)

$-1(4-3x-x^2)$

$-4+3x+x^2$

$=x^2+3x-4$

The answer should be written in descending order.

5. $6x+3x^2+5-2x-x^2-3$

$2x^2+4x+2$

$2(x^2+2x+1)$

$a+b=2$

$a(b)=1$

$2(x+1)(x+1)$

Practice Quiz

Answers and Solutions

1. D

By definition, a trinomial has three terms.

3. B

5. A like term for 7*xyz* must have *xyz* but can have any other numerical coefficient (using 7 would make it an identical term). A like term for $16y^3$ must have the y^3 and any numerical coefficient except 16 for the reasons above.

7. There will be twelve terms, as $(3)(2)(2) = 12$. Simplification may reduce this in later steps.

9. D

The answer can be confirmed by substitution, distribution, and simplification.

Lesson 6 Factoring a Difference of Squares

PRACTICE EXERCISES
Answers and Solutions

1. This becomes $(x+6)(x-6)$.

3. $x^8 - 16$

$(x^4+4)(x^4-4)$

$(x^4+4)(x^2+2)(x^2-2)$

5. B

$9x^2 - 49$

$(3x+7)(3x-7)$

$a = 3$

$b = 7$

$(a)(b) = 21$

Lesson 7 Factoring Using Decomposition of Polynomials

PRACTICE EXERCISES
Answers and Solutions

1. A

The polynomial becomes $x^2+9x-4x-36$ in the decomposition step, with the middle terms adding to 5 and multiplying to –36.

3. B

These two terms add to the original middle term, and the product of the coefficients is equal to the product of the leading coefficient and the constant term.

5. $6y^2 + 7y - 20$

$6y^2 - 8y + 15y - 20$

$2y(3y-4) + 5(3y-4)$

$(2y+5)(3y-4)$

Lesson 8 Division of a Polynomial

PRACTICE EXERCISES
Answers and Solutions

*Note: Outside of the lesson examples, the long division steps are not shown. By using the division statements, any answer can be verified by multiplying the quotient by the divisor, adding any remainder, and thus, restoring the original polynomial.

1. The quotient is $4m^2 + 2m + 1$. No remainder.

3. $P = (Q)(D) + R$

$(5x-1)(x+3) + 3$

$5x(x+3) - 1(x+3) + 3$

$5x^2 + 15x - x - 3 + 3$

$5x^2 + 14x$

5. $P = (Q)(D) + R$

In this case, the divisor is given as $2x$ and the remainder as 23. The quotient is not given, so then you must decide (create) the quotient before the polynomial can be found.

For one example, you may choose $(x+1)$ as the quotient.

$$polynomial = (x+1)(2x)+23$$
$$= 2x^2 + 2x + 23$$

This polynomial meets the requirements. Many answers are possible, so long as the division statement is used to ensure a correct answer.

Practice Test

Answers and Solutions

1. The first term is degree 3, the second is degree 1, and the third term is degree 2. The variables involved are $x, y,$ and z.

3. **D**

   $(1)(8x)$ $(-1)(-8x)$
   $(2)(4x)$ $(-2)(-4x)$
   $(4)(2x)$ $(-4)(-2x)$
   $(8)(x)$ $(-8)(-x)$

   $8x$ has 16 different factors.

   Note that each pair represents two factors.

5. By decomposition, $(a)(b) = 30$ and $a + b = 13$, so use 10 and 3.

   $2x^2 + 10x + 3x + 15$
   $2x(x+5) + 3(x+5)$
   $(2x+3)(x+5)$

7. By the law of exponents, $x^a x^b = x^{a+b}$. If $x^3 x^a = x^6$, then $a = 3$.

9. $P = (D)(Q) + R$

   $(y+3)(y+4)$
   $y^2 + 7y + 12$

   The unknown dividend is the trinomial $y^2 + 7y + 12$.

RATIONAL EXPRESSIONS

Lesson 1 Introduction to Rational Expressions and Non-Permissible Values

PRACTICE EXERCISES
Answers and Solutions

1. **B**

   This expression is rational because the radical sign ($\sqrt{}$) in the denominator does not include the variable.

3. **a)** Numerator: $(x+2) = 0$ and $2x = 0$

   Denominator: $(x-2) = 0$ and $x = 0$

   b) Numerator: $(x^2 - 1) = 0$

   Denominator: $(x^2 - 4) = 0$

5. The values of concern are in the denominator, and are found when $x^2 - 36 = 0$. This equation has the following solution:

   $x^2 = 36$
   $x = \pm 6$

   Note that this equation could have also been solved by factoring the polynomial as a difference of squares and solving as $(x+6)(x-6) = 0$.

   The solutions (which are the non-permissible values) would be the same as above.

   The non-permissible values are $x = \pm 6$.

Lesson 2 Simplifying Rational Expressions

PRACTICE EXERCISES
Answers and Solutions

1. A

3. $\dfrac{(x-2)}{(x-2)(x+3)}$

This expression can be reduced by cancelling the $(x-2)$ term, resulting in the simplest form of $\dfrac{1}{(x+3)}$. At the end, there appears to be only one NPV for x, but the original two NPVs are correct. The non-permissible values for x are 2, and -3.

5. C

This type of manipulation is key in determining common factors that can be cancelled (and common factors in difference of squares questions).

7. This could be written as a fraction with a polynomial that describes the gas volume in the numerator and a polynomial that describes the cubic space in the denominator. This is a rational expression.

$$\dfrac{x^3 + 2x^2}{(x+2)^3}$$

The denominator is cubed since the width is given as $x + 2$. Since it is a cube, the length and height are the same as the width.

$$\dfrac{(x)(x)(x+2)}{(x+2)^3}$$

$$\dfrac{x^2}{(x+2)^2}$$

This is the most reduced form as a rational expression. It could be written as a ratio as $x^2 : (x+2)^2$.

To find the restrictions on the variable, observe the initial denominator and solve.

$$(x+2)^3 = 0$$
$$x+2 = 0$$
$$x = -2$$

So, $x \neq -2$.

*Note that this is the complete answer. However, since the value of $x+2$ units is given as the width of an actual cubic space, if x were less than 2, there would have been a negative dimension to the object and this would not exist in real space.

Lesson 3 Multiplying Rational Expressions

PRACTICE EXERCISES
Answers and Solutions

1. $\dfrac{(x+1)^3}{24x} \times \dfrac{12x}{2(x^2 - 1)}$

$$\dfrac{(x+1)^3}{2(2)(x+1)(x-1)}$$

$$\dfrac{(x+1)^2}{4(x-1)}$$

This form is as reduced as is necessary (there are no further common terms).

$$24x = 0$$
$$x = 0$$
$$2x^2 - 2 = 0$$
$$2x^2 = 2$$
$$x^2 = 1$$
$$x = \pm 1$$

The restrictions on the variable are $x \neq 0, 1, -1$.

3. C

5. Answers will vary. The two rational expressions must simplify (after multiplication) to give the $\dfrac{2}{x}$ result and should be more complex (i.e., there should be some common factors to cancel).

An example is $\dfrac{2(x+1)}{x} \cdot \dfrac{1}{(x+1)}$. The restrictions for this are $x \neq 0, -1$.

Note that the restrictions for the variable will always include an NPV of $x = 0$.

7. **C**

Lesson 4 Dividing Rational Expressions

PRACTICE EXERCISES
Answers and Solutions

1. $\dfrac{5}{\left(\dfrac{20}{x^2}\right)}$ can be rewritten as $\dfrac{5}{1} \div \dfrac{20}{x^2}$, and then

switched to $\dfrac{5}{1} \times \dfrac{x^2}{20}$, which simplifies to $\dfrac{x^2}{4}$.
From the first step, the restriction $x \neq 0$ remains.

3. **A**

One method for solving this is to investigate what factor must be multiplied by $\dfrac{x}{3}$ to

result in $\dfrac{2}{x}$. The final denominator has x, whereas the first expression has an x in the numerator, so the missing expression must have an x^2 in the denominator. Also, the initial expression has a 3 in the denominator, and the final expression has a 2 in the numerator, so the missing expression must have a 6 in the numerator.

So, $\dfrac{6}{x^2}$ the reciprocal of this will give the missing expression from the division statement.

5. $4(1-x)$

$$\dfrac{\dfrac{x}{x-1}}{2x}$$

$$\dfrac{4(-1)(x-1)}{x} \div \dfrac{x-1}{2x}$$

$$\dfrac{-4(x-1)}{x} \times \dfrac{2x}{(x-1)}$$

$$-8$$

To find the non-permissible values, look at the original denominators and then the reciprocal denominator, then determine when they become zero.

$$x = 0$$
$$2x = 0$$
$$x = 0$$
$$(x-1) = 0$$
$$x = 1$$

So, $x \neq 0, 1$.

7. **A**–True

It is true that the restricted values are found only in the denominator. When an expression is replaced by its reciprocal the new denominator can produce new restricted values.

B–False

When simplifying, it is true that common factors can disappear, but the NPVs are considered before the cancelling. So, NPVs are not lost.

C–True

This is a true statement.

D–True

Any fraction with a denominator of zero is undefined.

Practice Quiz

Answers and Solutions

1. **A**–True

B–False

The expression is rational because the variable is in a radical.

C–False

The expression is rational.

D–False

This statement is false because division by zero is not permissible

3. **D**

It cannot be reduced. The other answers represent some of the common early mistakes made through cancelling.

5. The NPVs are found by determining when the denominators are equal to zero. This is when

$$x + 1 = 0$$
$$x = -1$$
$$x + 2 = 0 \quad \text{and so on, up to } x = -10$$
$$x = -2$$

So, all the NPVs are
$$x \neq -1, -2, -3, ..., -9, -10.$$

7. **A**

The question does not ask for the expression to be simplified or reduced, only for the NPVs. So, it is necessary to look at the denominators (and new denominators formed by reciprocals).
The numerator on the last term may tempt some to list -3 as an additional NPV, but this is not the case.

Lesson 5 Addition and Subtraction of Rational Expressions

PRACTICE EXERCISES
Answers and Solutions

1. $\dfrac{2}{3x} + \dfrac{3x}{4} - 1$

The lowest common denominator is $(3x)(4)$. Note that the denominator for the third term is just 1.

$$\frac{8}{(3x)(4)} + \frac{9x}{(3x)(4)} - \frac{12x}{(3x)(4)}$$

$$\frac{8 + 9x - 12x}{12x}$$

$$\frac{8 - 3x}{12x}$$

NPV is $x \neq 0$

3. $\dfrac{9y}{4} - \dfrac{x}{2} = \dfrac{y}{4}$

$$\frac{9y}{4} - \frac{2x}{4} = \frac{y}{4}$$

$$\frac{9y - 2x}{4} = \frac{y}{4}$$

$$9y - 2x = y$$

$$x = 4y$$

The solution shown solves this question step by step. At any point along the way, the solution may be stated by observation.

5. $\dfrac{x^2 - 6x - 7}{x + 1} - \dfrac{2x + 12}{2x + 2} + \dfrac{x + 1}{x^2 - 1}$

$$\frac{(x+1)(x-7)}{x+1} - \frac{2(x+6)}{2(x+1)} + \frac{(x+1)}{(x+1)(x-1)}$$

The first expression can be reduced by cancelling the common factors. But, by noting the other terms, a common denominator is going to include an $(x+1)$ factor, so leave this unsimplified.

The second expression should be simplified by cancelling the common factor of 2.

$$\frac{(x+1)(x-7)(x-1)}{(x+1)(x-1)} - \frac{(x+6)(x-1)}{(x+1)(x-1)} + \frac{(x+1)}{(x+1)(x-1)}$$

$$\frac{x^3 - 5x^2 - 13x - 7 - x^2 - 5x + 6 + x + 1}{(x+1)(x-1)}$$

$$\frac{x^3 - 6x^2 - 17x}{(x+1)(x-1)}$$

$$x \neq 1, -1$$

Lesson 6 Rational Equations and Problem Solving

PRACTICE EXERCISES
Answers and Solutions

1. Multiply by the LCM of the denominator, which is $(x-1)(x)$. This was found after ensuring that each expression was simplified. At this initial step, the NPVs for the variable are determined to be $x \neq 1, 0$.

$$\frac{2(x-1)(x)}{x-1} = \frac{3(x-1)(x)}{x}$$
$$2x = 3(x-1)$$
$$2x = 3x - 3$$
$$0 = x - 3$$
$$3 = x$$

The answer of $x = 3$ can be verified by substitution into the original equation.

$$\frac{2}{(3-1)} = \frac{3}{(3)}$$
$$\frac{2}{2} = \frac{3}{3}$$
$$1 = 1$$

So, this is a true solution, and it is not a non-permissible value.

3. $$\frac{x}{x+1} = \frac{-2}{2x+2}$$
   $$\frac{x}{x+1} = \frac{-1}{x+1}$$

After factoring and cancelling a factor of 2 from the second expression, it is possible to continue solving using the set steps or to solve by observation.

Since both denominators are the same, for the equality to be true, the numerators must also be equal. This means that $x = -1$. However by noting any NPVs, it is found that $x \neq -1$. The only solution to this equation is non-permissible, so there are no solutions.

5. Solve by multiplying each expression by the LCM.

$$13 = 4(y+1)$$
$$13 = 4y + 4$$
$$9 = 4y$$
$$y = \frac{9}{4}$$

Practice Test

Answers and Solutions

1. **D**

   This answer reduces to the given expression through factoring and cancelling a common factor of 2. The other answers reflect some common mistakes in factoring and cancelling.

---

3. **A**–False

The variable x need not be introduced.

B–False

Cancelling common factors does not eliminate the need to list original NPVs that those factors included.

C–False

This answer has the wrong variable.

D–True

After a common factor of 2 is cancelled, a rational expression that satisfies the condition is created.

5. First, simplify:

$$\frac{(x+2)(x-3)}{(x-a)^2} \div \frac{x^2-x-6}{x-1}$$

$$\frac{(x+2)(x-3)}{(x-a)^2} \times \frac{(x-1)}{(x+2)(x-3)}$$

$$\frac{(x-1)}{(x-a)^2}$$

In order for the numerator to simplify to 1, there must be a common factor in the denominator to cancel the $(x-1)$ remaining in the numerator. This means that the denominator is actually $(x-1)^2$, and so $a=1$. The expression then simplifies to

$$\frac{1}{(x-1)}$$

The non-permissible values found throughout the simplification process are found as follows:

$$x-1=0$$
$$x=1$$
$$x+2=0$$
$$x=-2$$
$$x-3=0$$
$$x=3$$

$x \neq 1, -2, 3$. $a=1$ is allowed even though $x \neq 1$, since a is not x.

7. $\dfrac{x}{2}+\dfrac{x}{4}=10$

$$\frac{2x}{4}+\frac{x}{4}=\frac{40}{4}$$

$$\frac{3x}{4}=\frac{40}{4}$$

$$3x=40$$

$$x=\frac{40}{3}$$

$$x=13\frac{1}{3}$$

The original number, expressed as a fraction, is $\dfrac{40}{3}$.

Now, verify:

One half of $\dfrac{40}{3}$ is $\dfrac{20}{3}$. One quarter of $\dfrac{40}{3}$ is $\dfrac{10}{3}$. Added together, these equal $\dfrac{30}{3}$ or 10. The answer is verified.

9. Each of the smaller boxes has a side length of 5 cm. To minimize the volume of the larger box, it is desirable to minimize the empty space.
For example, if the 10 boxes were simply placed in a square, five boxes by five boxes, this would contain all of them, but would require the larger box to have dimensions of 5(5) by 5(5) cm for a base. Since the large box is a cube, it would also have to be 25 cm tall. That would be a lot of wasted space, since the small boxes would only fill the bottom 5 cm of the height.

Consider the case of two small boxes on a side. In this case, two boxes by two boxes would only account for 4 boxes, so they would have to be stacked three levels high. This would require a large box with dimensions of 15 cm per side (remember the larger box is a cube, so if the small boxes are stacked three high, that requires a larger box with dimensions 15 cm). The volume of this box is $(15 \text{ cm})^3$.

Consider the case of three small boxes on a side. This would account for nine boxes on the first layer, but would require a second layer (for a single small box). The volume for this larger box is identical to the case above, since the dimensions would be 3(5) cm per side.

Any arrangement of the small boxes greater than three per side would waste excess space, and the only arrangement smaller than two small boxes per side would be a single tower of the 10 small boxes, requiring a large box of dimensions 5(10) cm per side.

Therefore, the minimum volume required for the larger box is $V = \left(15 \text{ cm}^3\right)$

$$= 3\ 375 \text{ cm}^3$$

EXPONENTS AND RADICALS

Lesson 1 Number Sets

PRACTICE EXERCISES
Answers and Solutions

1.
4   *Natural*
0   *Whole*
−3   *Integer*
1.44   *Rational*
$\sqrt{3}$ *Irrational*

3. This decimal terminates after four decimal places. Any decimal that terminates or repeats is rational, so this is a rational number (even though x and y are unknown).

5. The set of real numbers, $\mathbb{R}$.

Lesson 2 Calculations with Real Numbers

PRACTICE EXERCISES
Answers and Solutions

1. The square root of 16 is 4. Taking the square root of 4 gives 2. The same answer is found by using the calculator and finding the square root of the square root of 16.

3. The numbers, rounded to three decimal places, are 1.414, 1.732, and 0.286. Adding them produces 3.432 as an answer. This rounded to the nearest hundredth is 3.43. The same numbers rounded to two decimal places are 1.41, 1.73, and 0.29. Adding them produces 3.43 as an answer. The first answer is more accurate since there are more decimal places, but rounded to the nearest hundredth, the first answer would still produce the second answer.

5. The smallest is $(-3)^2 = 9$. The next largest is $\sqrt[3]{1\ 000} = 10$. The largest is $|-32| = 32$.

Lesson 3 Radicals and Exponents

PRACTICE EXERCISES
Answers and Solutions

1. $13^{\frac{3}{5}}$

3. $\left(\dfrac{2}{x}\right)^3 = \dfrac{2^3}{x^3} = \dfrac{8}{x^3}$

5. $\dfrac{2^3}{8} = \dfrac{2^3}{2^3} = 2^{3-3} = 2^0 = 1$

Lesson 4 Using Exponent Laws to Simplify, Evaluate, and Identify Patterns

PRACTICE EXERCISES
Answers and Solutions

1. **a)** Each subsequent number in a pattern is the product of the previous term and $\frac{1}{4}$ or 4^{-1}. The next term in the sequence is 4^{-3} or $\frac{1}{64}$.

b) $4^{-3} = \frac{1}{4^3}$

$4^{-3} = \frac{1}{64}$

3. $1.5 \times 3^{\left(\frac{60}{6}\right)} = 88\ 573.5$

The hot dog will cost $88 573.50 in 60 years.

5. **a)** $n^5 \div n^3 = 25$

$n^{(5-3)} = 25$

$n^2 = 25$

$n = \sqrt{25}$

$n = 5 \text{ or } -5$

b) $\left(n^3\right)^2 = 729$

$n^{(3 \times 2)} = 729$

$n^6 = 729$

$\sqrt{n^6} = \sqrt{729}$

$\sqrt{n^3 \times n^3} = \sqrt{27 \times 27}$

$n^3 = 27$

$n = \sqrt[3]{27}$

$n = 3$

c) $n^8 \times n^{-12} = \frac{1}{256}$

$n^{(8-12)} = \frac{1}{2^8}$

$\frac{1}{n^4} = \frac{1}{2^8}$

$n^4 = 2^8$

$\sqrt[4]{n^4} = \sqrt[4]{2^8}$

$n = 2^2$

$n = 4$

Lesson 5 Using Exponent Laws to Simplify Questions Involving Coefficients and Variables and to Evaluate Complex Numerical Questions

PRACTICE EXERCISES
Answers and Solutions

1. **a)** $\left(x^{-3}\right)^2 = x^{(-3 \times 2)}$

$= x^{-6}$

b) $\left(\frac{m^2 n^3}{mn^{-2}}\right) = m^{(2-1)} n^{(3+2)}$

$= mn^5$

c) $\frac{x^4 y^7 z^{-3}}{x^2 y^{-5} z^2} = x^{(4-2)} y^{(7+5)} z^{(-3-2)}$

$= x^2 y^{12} z^{-5}$

d) $(4g^3 h^5)(-5g^{-4} h^3) = (4 \times -5)g^{(3-4)} h^{(5+3)}$

$= -20g^{-1} h^8$

e) $(3g^{-5} h^5)(5g^{-4} h^3) = (3 \times 5)g^{(-5-4)} h^{(5+3)}$

$= 15g^{-9} h^8$

f) $(ab^{-3})^{-5} = a^{(1 \times -5)} b^{(-3 \times -5)}$

$= a^{-5} b^{15}$

g) $\frac{-36a^5 b^{-3}}{-12a^6 b^{-5}} = (-36 \div -12)a^{(5-6)} b^{(-3+5)}$

$= 3a^{-1} b^2$

h) $\left(\frac{m^2 n^{-3}}{m^4 n}\right)^2 = (m^{(2-4)} n^{(-3-1)})^2$

$= (m^{-2} n^{-4})^2$

$= m^{-4} n^{-8}$

i) $\left(6x^2 y^{-4}\right)\left(-12y^5\right) = \left(6\times -12\right)x^2 y^{(-4-5)}$

$$= -72x^2 y^{-9}$$

j) $\dfrac{12a^3 b^{-3}}{-18a^5 b^2} = \left(12 \div -18\right)a^{(3-5)}b^{(-3-2)}$

$$= -\dfrac{2}{3}a^{-2}b^{-5} \text{ or } \dfrac{-2}{3a^2 b^5}$$

Practice Quiz

Answers and Solutions

1. Only one number, 0, differs. The whole numbers are the naturals plus 0.

3. **B**

   Since the first number is irrational, it neither terminates nor repeats. Since it does not terminate, multiplying by 2 would still not terminate. Answer **A** is incorrect since there is a correct answer.

5. Knowing the squares of the first ten or so integers, you will know that 5 is the same as $\sqrt{25}$. Or vice-versa, knowing that root 25 is 5. $\sqrt{26}$ is larger than $\sqrt{25}$, so it is also larger than 5.

7. $3 \div \left(\sqrt{3} \times \sqrt[3]{3}\right)$

   $3^1 \div 3^{\frac{1}{2}+\frac{1}{3}}$ Using laws of exponents (same base):

   $3^{1-\frac{5}{6}}$

   $3^{\frac{1}{6}}$

   By calculator, $\sqrt[6]{3} = 1.200\ 93\ \dots$

   This decimal does not repeat or terminate, so the number is irrational.

Lesson 6 Simplifying Radicals

PRACTICE EXERCISES
Answers and Solutions

1. The answer is not correct for two reasons. First, the investigation of radicals shows that radicals cannot be added or subtracted in this way. Secondary root 25 equals 5 and root 9 is 3. This difference is 2, as opposed to the proposed answer of root 16, which is 4.

3. Factor, looking for perfect squares:
   $\sqrt{98} = \sqrt{(2)(49)} = 7\sqrt{2}$

5. $\sqrt[3]{27x^3 y^9 z^{12}}$

   $\sqrt[3]{3^3 x^3 \left(y^3\right)^3 \left(z^4\right)^3}$

   $3xy^3 z^4$

Lesson 7 Additions and Subtraction of Radicals

PRACTICE EXERCISES
Answers and Solutions

1. $3\sqrt{17} - \sqrt{34}$. These two radicals are not a like radically so they cannot be added. They are also in their most simplified forms.

3. **B**

   $\sqrt{99} = \sqrt{(9)(11)} = 3\sqrt{11}$

   This answer is then added to the like radical term.

5. Simplify to mixed radicals:

   $4\sqrt{2} - 3\sqrt{2} = \sqrt{2}$

Lesson 8 Multiplication and Division of Radicals

PRACTICE EXERCISES
Answers and Solutions

1. Multiply numerical coefficients and radicals, then simplify if needed:

$$(2)(3)\left(\sqrt{2}\right)\left(\sqrt{2}\right)$$
$$6(2)$$
$$12$$

3. Multiplying three radicals follows the same pattern as multiplying two.

$$(12)(2)(2)\left(\sqrt{2}\right)\left(\sqrt{3}\right)\left(\sqrt{2}\right)$$
$$48(2)\sqrt{3}$$
$$96\sqrt{3}$$

5. The radicals can be reduced and common factors cancelled before rationalizing is required.
This makes the rationalizing process simpler. One set of steps that renders at the final, correct answer is shown below.

$$\frac{3\sqrt{72}}{2\sqrt{12}} = \frac{3\sqrt{36(2)}}{2\sqrt{4(3)}} = \frac{(3)(6)\sqrt{2}}{(2)(2)\sqrt{3}} = \frac{9\sqrt{2}}{2\sqrt{3}}$$

$$\frac{9\sqrt{2}}{2\sqrt{3}}\left(\frac{\sqrt{3}}{\sqrt{3}}\right) = \frac{9\sqrt{6}}{2(3)} = \frac{3\sqrt{6}}{2}$$

Practice Test

Answers and Solutions

1. **C**

By definition, an irrational number as a decimal does not terminate or repeat.

3. A rational number is a number that can be represented by $\frac{a}{b}$, where a and b are integers and $b \neq 0$. Rewriting an irrational number as a fraction does not change the fact that the numerator is still an irrational number and not an integer.

5. According to the Pythagorean theorem, the sides of a right triangle are defined by $a^2 + b^2 = c^2$.

$$\left(2+\sqrt{3}\right)^2 + \left(3+\sqrt{3}\right)^2 = \left(x+\sqrt{3}\right)^2$$
$$x = \sqrt{\left(2+\sqrt{3}\right)^2 + \left(3+\sqrt{3}\right)^2} - \sqrt{3}$$

Only the positive square root needs to be considered since the length of the third side must be greater than either of the other two sides, and it certainly cannot be a negative length. The formula above, properly entered into a calculator or calculated remembering the Order of Operations, would produce a value for x.

7. **A**

The correct answer reduces to 4, or 2^2.

9. $$\frac{\sqrt{64-16}}{\sqrt{3}}$$

$$\frac{\sqrt{48}}{\sqrt{3}}\left(\frac{\sqrt{3}}{\sqrt{3}}\right)$$
$$\frac{4\sqrt{3}}{\sqrt{3}}\left(\frac{\sqrt{3}}{\sqrt{3}}\right)$$
$$\frac{4(3)}{3}$$
$$4$$

11. $$\frac{\left(\sqrt{3}+1\right)\left(\sqrt{3}-1\right)}{\sqrt{5}+2}$$

$$\frac{\sqrt{3}\sqrt{3}-1\sqrt{3}+1\sqrt{3}+1(-1)}{\sqrt{5}+2}\left(\frac{\sqrt{5}-2}{\sqrt{5}-2}\right)$$

$$\frac{(3-1)\left(\sqrt{5}-2\right)}{\sqrt{5}\sqrt{5}+2\sqrt{5}-2\sqrt{5}-2(2)}$$

$$\frac{2\sqrt{5}-4}{5-4}$$

$$2\sqrt{5}-4$$

LINE SEGMENTS AND GRAPHS

Lesson 1 Plotting Linear and Non-Linear Data

PRACTICE EXERCISES
Answers and Solutions

1. A

The graph is a straight line and the points are connected.

3. a) Discrete

   b) Continuous

   c) Discrete

   d) Continuous

5. a)

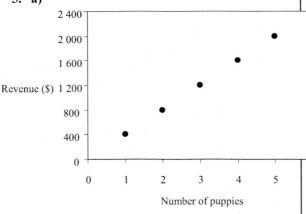

Number of puppies

b) The graph is linear.

c) $[0, 6, 1] \times [0, 2\,400, 400]$

Lesson 2 The Distance Between Points

PRACTICE EXERCISES
Answers and Solutions

1. C

3. a) $d = \sqrt{(2+6)^2 + (-1-2)^2}$

   $d = \sqrt{64+9}$

   $d = \sqrt{73}$

   $d \approx 8.5$

   b) $d = \sqrt{(12+20)^2 + (40+5)^2}$

   $d = \sqrt{32^2 + 5^2}$

   $d = \sqrt{3\,049}$

   $d \approx 55.2$

5. Length of $\overline{AB}$ $= \sqrt{(3-(-3))^2 + (2-3)^2}$

   $= \sqrt{37}$

   Length of $\overline{BC}$ $= \sqrt{((-1)-3)^2 + (-4-2)^2}$

   $= \sqrt{52}$

   Length of $\overline{CA}$
   $= \sqrt{(-3-(-1))^2 + (3-(-4))^2}$

   $= \sqrt{53}$

   Since all three sides have a different length, the triangle is scalene.

Lesson 3 The Midpoint of the Segment

PRACTICE EXERCISES
Answers and Solutions

1. B

$$M = \left(\frac{x_1 + x_2}{2}, \frac{y_1 + y_2}{2} \right)$$

$$M = \left(\frac{4 - 6}{2}, \frac{-7 - 3}{2} \right)$$

$$M = (-1, -5)$$

3. a) By inspection, the midpoint is at $(-1, 4)$:

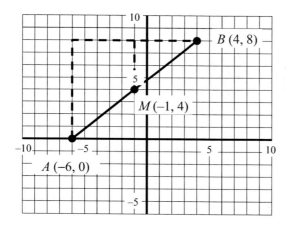

b) $M = \left(\frac{x_1 + x_2}{2}, \frac{y_1 + y_2}{2} \right)$

$$M = \left(\frac{12 - 2}{2}, \frac{-7 + 11}{2} \right)$$

$$M = (5, 2)$$

c) $M = \left(\frac{\frac{3}{2} - \frac{5}{2}}{2}, \frac{5 - 8}{2} \right)$

$$M = \left(\frac{-1}{2}, \frac{-3}{2} \right)$$

5. First, find the midpoint of AB:

$$M = \left(\frac{x_1 + x_2}{2}, \frac{y_1 + y_2}{2} \right)$$

$$M = \left(\frac{-10 + 4}{2}, \frac{3 + 7}{2} \right)$$

$$M = (-3, 5)$$

Now, use the distance formula to find the distance between M and C.

$$d = \sqrt{(x_2 - x_1)^2 + (y_2 - y_1)^2}$$

$$= \sqrt{(-3 - 0)^2 + (5 - (-2))^2}$$

$$= \sqrt{9 + 49}$$

$$= \sqrt{58}$$

$$d \approx 7.6 \text{ units}$$

The distance from the midpoint of $\overline{AB}$ to C is 7.6 units.

Lesson 4 Slope

PRACTICE EXERCISES
Answers and Solutions

1. C

To compare the four slopes, it is helpful to express the decimal equivalent of each.

$$\frac{1}{2} = 0.5$$

$$\frac{4}{6} \approx 0.667$$

$$\frac{10}{3} \approx 3.33$$

$$2 = 2$$

3. a) Count the rise and run:

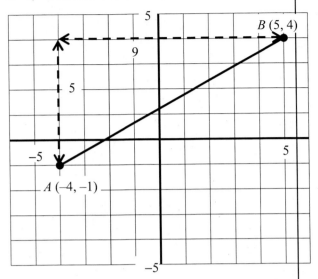

$$m = \frac{\text{rise}}{\text{run}}$$

$$m = \frac{5}{9}$$

b) $m = \dfrac{y_2 - y_1}{x_2 - x_1}$

$$m = \frac{1 - (-2)}{12 - 3}$$

$$= \frac{3}{9}$$

$$m = \frac{1}{3}$$

c) $m = \dfrac{y_2 - y_1}{x_2 - x_1}$

$$m = \frac{7 - 7}{-2 - 2}$$

$$= \frac{0}{4}$$

$$m = 0$$

d) $m = \dfrac{y_2 - y_1}{x_2 - x_1}$

$$m = \frac{4 - 1}{-5(-5)}$$

$$= \frac{3}{0}, \quad \text{which is undefined}$$

5. Sketch the graph and then count using the rise and run to locate points.

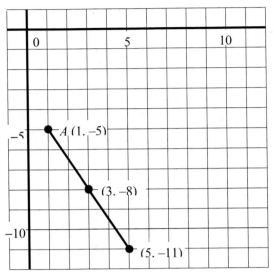

$(3, -8)$ and $(5, -11)$ are two possible correct answers.

Lesson 5 Slopes of Parallel and Perpendicular Lines

PRACTICE EXERCISES
Answers and Solutions

1.

Slope of l	Slope of line parallel to l	Slope of line perpendicular to l
$\dfrac{5}{7}$	$\dfrac{5}{7}$	$-\dfrac{7}{5}$
$-\dfrac{3}{5}$	$-\dfrac{3}{5}$	$\dfrac{5}{3}$
4	4	$-\dfrac{1}{4}$
$-\dfrac{1}{3}$	$-\dfrac{1}{3}$	3
0	0	undefined

3. A

Find the slope of $\overline{AB}$:

$$m = \frac{y_2 - y_1}{x_2 - x_1}$$

$$m = \frac{3+1}{7+13}$$

$$m = \frac{1}{5}$$

Determine the slope of each alternative.

Line segments with the points $C\,(0, 3)$ and $D\,(5, 4)$ are parallel to line AB because they have the same slope.

5. Find the slope of $\overline{AB}$:

$$m = \frac{y_2 - y_1}{x_2 - x_1}$$

$$m = \frac{3-1}{3+2}$$

$$m = \frac{2}{5}$$

Since $\overline{CD}$ is perpendicular, it will have a slope of $-\dfrac{5}{2}$.

Since D is on the x-axis, its coordinates are $(x, 0)$.

For $\overline{CD}$:

$$m = \frac{y_2 - y_1}{x_2 - x_1}$$

$$\frac{-5}{2} = \frac{0-5}{x-1}$$

$$-5(x-1) = 2(-5)$$

$$-5x = -15$$

$$x = 3$$

The coordinates of D are $(3, 0)$.

Answers and Solutions

1. B

The relationship is discrete because the points are not connected, and non-linear because the points do not lie in a straight line.

3. A

$$d = \sqrt{\left(x_2 - x_1\right)^2 + \left(y_2 - y_1\right)^2}$$

$$= \sqrt{\left(-2+5\right)^2 + \left(1-3\right)^2}$$

$$= \sqrt{9+4}$$

$$d = \sqrt{13}$$

5. $M = \left(\dfrac{x_1 + x_2}{2}, \dfrac{y_1 + y_2}{2}\right)$

$$(-7, 1) = \left(\frac{1+x}{2}, \frac{-3+y}{2}\right)$$

x-coordinate: $\qquad$ y-coordinate:

$$-7 = \frac{1+x}{2} \qquad 1 = \frac{-3+y}{2}$$

$$-14 = 1+x \qquad 2 = -3+y$$

$$-15 = x \qquad 5 = y$$

Point B is located at $(-15, 5)$.

7. a) The centre of the circle is the midpoint of the diameter.

$$M = \left(\frac{2+6}{2}, \frac{-11-3}{2}\right)$$

$$= (4, -7)$$

b) The circumference of a circle is found with the formula $C = 2\pi r$.

The radius is equal to the distance between the centre and a point on the circle.

$$d = \sqrt{(4-2)^2 + (-7+11)^2}$$
$$= \sqrt{4+16}$$
$$= \sqrt{20}$$
$$= 2\sqrt{5}$$

$$C = 2\pi r$$
$$= 2\pi \left(2\sqrt{5} \right)$$
$$= 28.10 \text{ units}$$

Lesson 6 The Equation of a Line
$y = mx + b$

PRACTICE EXERCISES
Answers and Solutions

1. C

$$5x - 2y = 6$$
$$-2y = -5x + 6$$
$$y = \frac{5}{2}x - 3$$

$$m = \frac{5}{2}$$

3. $m = -4$

$$b = \frac{1}{2}$$

$$y = mx + b$$
$$y = -4x + \frac{1}{2}$$

5. a)

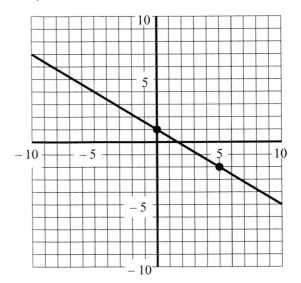

b) $5x - 2y + 6 = 0$

$$y = \frac{5}{2}x + 3$$

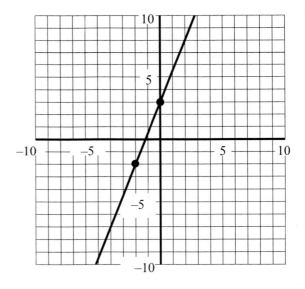

Lesson 7 The Equation of a Line Given Unique Characteristics

PRACTICE EXERCISES
Answers and Solutions

1. C

The sign of the slope is part of the slope. This does not provide a location for the line.

3. C

The slope of the perpendicular line is $-\dfrac{4}{7}$, so the required slope is $\dfrac{7}{4}$. An *x*-intercept of –2 can be written as (–2, 0).

Practice Test

Answers and Solutions

1. C

There is no price for partial cupcakes.

3. C

Negative

5. Slope of $\overline{AB}$: Slope of $\overline{BC}$:

$$m = \frac{y_2 - y_1}{x_2 - x_1}$$

$$m = \frac{6 - 1}{-1 + 3}$$

$$m = \frac{5}{2}$$

$$m = \frac{y_2 - y_1}{x_2 - x_1}$$

$$m = \frac{16 - 6}{3 - (-1)}$$

$$m = \frac{10}{4}$$

$$= \frac{5}{2}$$

Since the slopes of $\overline{AB}$ and $\overline{BC}$ are equal, the points are collinear.

7. C

Isosceles. The triangle has two equal sides.

Length of $\overline{AB}$:

$$d = \sqrt{(x_2 - x_1)^2 + (y_2 - y_2)^2}$$

$$= \sqrt{(-4 - 1)^2 + (-2 - 6)^2}$$

$$= \sqrt{25 + 64}$$

$$= \sqrt{89}$$

Length of $\overline{BC}$:

$$d = \sqrt{(6 - (-4))^2 + (-2 - (-2))^2}$$

$$= \sqrt{100}$$

$$= 10$$

Length of $\overline{CA}$

$$d = \sqrt{(6 - 1)^2 + (-2 - 6)^2}$$

$$= \sqrt{5^2 + 8^2}$$

$$= \sqrt{89}$$

9. a) $m = \dfrac{2}{7}$

1st point (–4, 6)
2nd point (*x*, *y*)

$$m = \frac{y_2 - y_1}{x_2 - x_1}$$

$$\frac{2}{7} = \frac{y - 6}{x + 4}$$

$$2x + 8 = 7y - 42$$

$$2x - 7y + 50 = 0$$

b) $m = \dfrac{1 - 2}{3 + 5}$

$$m = -\frac{1}{8}$$

1st point (–5, 2)
2nd point (*x*, *y*)

$$m = \frac{y_2 - y_1}{x_2 - x_1}$$

$$\frac{-1}{8} = \frac{y - 2}{x + 5}$$

$$-x - 5 = 8y - 16$$

$$-x - 8y + 11 = 0$$

$$x + 8y - 11 = 0$$

c) Slope of given line:

$$3x - 5y + 10 = 0$$

$$-5y = -3x - 10$$

$$y = \frac{3}{5}x + 2$$

$$m = \frac{3}{5}$$

Slope of perpendicular line $m = -\frac{5}{3}$

1st point $(-6, 0)$

2nd point (x, y)

$$m = \frac{y_2 - y_1}{x_2 - x_1}$$

$$\frac{-5}{3} = \frac{y}{x + 6}$$

$$-5x - 30 = 3y$$

$$-5x - 3y - 30 = 0$$

$$5x + 3y + 30 = 0$$

d) $m = \dfrac{-2 - (-5)}{1 - (-3)}$

$$m = \frac{3}{4}$$

1st point $(1, -2)$
2nd point (x, y)

$$m = \frac{y_2 - y_1}{x_2 - x_1}$$

$$\frac{3}{4} = \frac{y + 2}{x - 1}$$

$$3x - 3 = 4y + 8$$

$$3x - 4y - 11 = 0$$

FUNCTIONS AND RELATIONS

Lesson 1 Function Models of Real-Life Situations

PRACTICE EXERCISES
Answers and Solutions

1. The velocity of the roller-coaster, when climbing, is usually steady—not increasing or decreasing. When it goes down the other side, the velocity is increasing.

3.

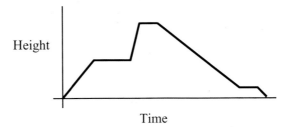

5. Answers will vary.

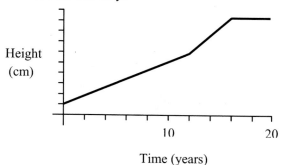

Height (cm)

Time (years)

Lesson 2 Functions

PRACTICE EXERCISES
Answers and Solutions

1. B

Some expressions relating two variables can have more than one output for each input and so, are not functions.

3. a) $f(x) = x^2 - 2x + 5$

$$f(-2) = (-2)^2 - 2(-2) + 5$$
$$f(-2) = 13$$

b) $f(x) = x^2 - 2x + 5$

$$f(7a) = (7a)^2 - 2(7a) + 5$$
$$f(7a) = 49a^2 - 14a + 5$$

c) $f(x) = x^2 - 2x + 5$

$$f(\sqrt{3}) = (\sqrt{3})^2 + 2(\sqrt{3})x + 5$$
$$f(\sqrt{3}) = 8 - 2\sqrt{3}$$

d) $f(x) = x^2 - 2x + 5$

$$f(s+3) = (s+3)^2 - 2(s+3) + 5$$
$$f(s+3) = s^2 + 6s + 9 - 2s - 6 + 5$$
$$f(s+3) = s^2 + 4s + 8$$

5. a) $f(-3) = 5$

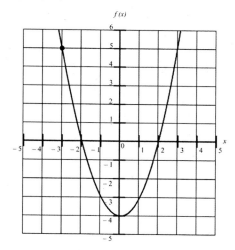

b) $f(0) = -4$

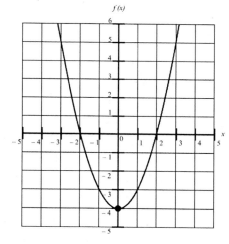

c) $f(2) = 0$

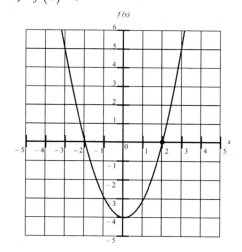

d) $f(x) = -3$

$x = \pm 1$

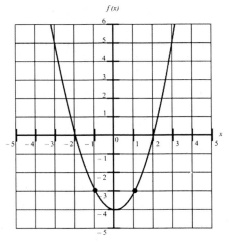

7. Words: "Six times a number."

Equation: $g(x) = 6x$

Lesson 3 Domain and Range

PRACTICE EXERCISES
Answers and Solutions

1. D

3. a) Domain: $x \le 2$ $x \ge 2$
    Range: $y \ge 0$ $y \le 0$

b) Domain: $x \ge -1$
    Range: $y \in \mathbb{R}$

c) Domain: $-1, 0, 2, 4$
    Range: $-3, 0, 1, 3$

d) Domain: $x \in \mathbb{R}$
    Range: $y \in \mathbb{R}$

e)

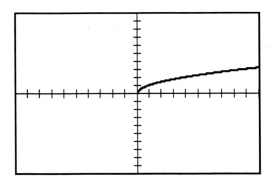

Domain: $x \ge 0$
Range: $y \ge 0$

f)

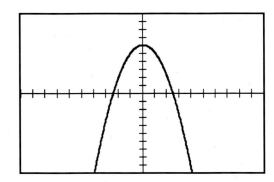

Domain: $x \in \mathbb{R}$
Range: $y \le 6$

Practice Quiz

Answers and Solutions

1. D

The segment from D to E is steepest.

3. a) A function is any set of ordered pairs that satisfies the condition that only one range value exists for each domain value.

b) Any three of: equation, words, graphs, ordered pairs, or table of values.

5. a) $f(x) = 2x^2 + x$

$$f(a-3) = 2(a-3)^2 + (a-3)$$
$$= 2(a^2 - 6a + 9) + a - 3$$
$$= 2a^2 - 12a + 18 + a - 3$$
$$= 2a^2 - 11a + 15$$

b) $f(x) = 2x^2 + x$

$$f(3\sqrt{6}) = 2(3\sqrt{6})^2 + (3\sqrt{6})$$
$$= 2(9(6)) + (3\sqrt{6})$$
$$= 108 + 3\sqrt{6}$$

7. a)

x	$f(x)$
-1	9
0	5
1	1

b)

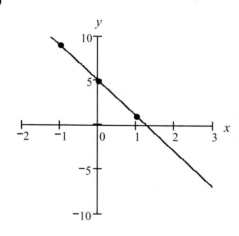

Lesson 4 Linear Functions

PRACTICE EXERCISES
Answers and Solutions

1. B

3. a) x-intercept:

$$(x, 0)$$
$$4x - 7y = 56$$
$$4x - 7(0) = 56$$
$$x = 14$$

y-intercept:

$$(0, y)$$
$$4x - 7y = 56$$
$$4(0) - 7y = 56$$
$$y = 8$$

b) x-intercept:

$$(x, 0)$$
$$5x - 4y + 25 = 0$$
$$5x - 4(0) + 25 = 0$$
$$x = -8$$

y-intercept:

$$(0, y)$$
$$5(0) - 4y + 25 = 0$$
$$-4y + 25 = 0$$
$$y = \frac{25}{4}$$
$$y = 6.25$$

5. a) Reading from the graph:

x-intercept: 500 or (500, 0)

y-intercept: 45 or (0, 45)

b) The x-intercept represents the tank being empty after driving 500 km.

The y-intercept represents a full tank before driving any distance.

---

c) Any two points can be used, such as (0, 45) and (500, 0).

$$m = \frac{y_2 - y_1}{x_2 - x_1}$$

$$m = \frac{0 - 45}{500 - 0}$$

$$m = -\frac{9}{100}$$

d) The slope represents the number (9) of litres of fuel consumed per 100 km of driving.

e) Domain: $0 \le d \le 500$
   Range: $0 \le F \le 45$

Lesson 5 Direct and Partial Variation

PRACTICE EXERCISES
Answers and Solutions

1. D

3. Let b be the phone bill and n be the number of minutes talked.

   a) $b = mn$

   $$16.52 = m(236)$$
   $$m = 0.07$$

   b) $b = 0.07n$

5. a) $s = mt$

   $$6 = m(5)$$
   $$m = 1.2$$

   b) $s = 1.2t$

   c)

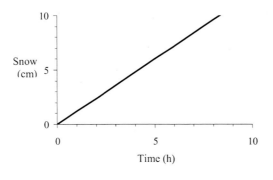

d) The slope indicates how much snow falls each hour.

e) 2 days = 48 hours

   $$s = 1.2(48)$$
   $$s = 57.6$$

57.6 cm of snow will fall in two days.

Practice Test

Answers and Solutions

1. C

There is more than one output for each input.

3. B

The statement that indicates that the graph includes the point (0, 0) is not true.

5. C

The slope is increasing, so the velocity is increasing.

7. Using the two intercepts, (0, 30) and (6, 0), as points:

$$m = \frac{y_2 - y_1}{x_2 - x_1}$$

$$m = \frac{0 - 30}{6 - 0}$$

$$m = -5$$

$$y = mx + b$$
$$y = -5x + 30$$

NOTES

NOTES

NOTES

ORDERING INFORMATION

SCHOOL ORDERS

Schools and school jurisdictions are eligible for our **educational discount** rate.
Contact Castle Rock Research BC for more information.

THE KEY **Study Guides** are specifically designed to assist students in preparing for unit tests, final exams, and provincial examinations.

THE KEY **Study Guides** – $29.95 each plus G.S.T.

SENIOR HIGH		JUNIOR HIGH	ELEMENTARY
Biology 12 Chemistry 12 English 12 Geography 12 History 12 Physics 12 Principles of Math 12	Biology 11 Chemistry 11 English 11 Physics 11 Principles of Math 11 Social Studies 11 English 10 Principles of Math 10 Science 10	Language Arts 9 Math 9 Language Arts 7 Math 7	Math 6 Language Arts 4 Math 4

Student Notes and Problems (SNAP) Workbooks contain complete examinations of curriculum concepts, examples, and exercise questions.

SNAP Workbooks – $29.95 each plus G.S.T.

SENIOR HIGH		JUNIOR HIGH	ELEMENTARY
Chemistry 12 Physics 12 Principles of Math 12	Chemistry 11 Physics 11 Principles of Math 11 Principles of Math 10 Science 10	Math 9 Science 9 Math 8 Math 7	Math 6 Math 5 Math 4 Math 3

For students in the following courses, the following resources are correlated to the B.C. curriculum.

B.C. Course Name	Corresponding Resources
Applications of Math 12	*THE KEY* – Math 30 Applied
	SNAP – Math 30 Applied
Applications of Math 10	**SNAP** – Math 10 Applied
Calculus 12	**SNAP** – Math 31

Visit our website for a tour of resource content and features, or order resources online at
www.castlerockresearch.com

#4-1905 Evergreen Court
Kelowna, BC V1Y 9L4
E-mail: learnbc@castlerockresearch.com

Phone: 250.868.8384
Toll-free: 866.882.8246
Fax: 250.868.9146

ORDER FORM

THE KEY	Price	Quantity	Total
Biology 12	$29.95		
Chemistry 12	$29.95		
English 12	$29.95		
Geography 12	$29.95		
History 12	$29.95		
Physics 12	$29.95		
Principles of Math 12	$29.95		
Biology 11	$29.95		
Chemistry 11	$29.95		
English 11	$29.95		
Physics 11	$29.95		
Principles of Math 11	$29.95		
Social Studies 11	$29.95		
English 10	$29.95		
Principles of Math 10	$29.95		
Science 10	$29.95		
Language Arts 9	$29.95		
Math 9	$29.95		
Language Arts 7	$29.95		
Math 7	$29.95		
Math 6	$29.95		
Language Arts 4	$29.95		
Math 4	$29.95		
Subtotal 1			

SNAP WORKBOOKS	Price	Quantity	Total
Chemistry 12	$29.95		
Physics 12	$29.95		
Principles of Math 12	$29.95		
Chemistry 11	$29.95		
Physics 11	$29.95		
Principles of Math 11	$29.95		
Principles of Math 10	$29.95		
Science 10	$29.95		
Math 9	$29.95		
Science 9	$29.95		
Math 8	$29.95		
Math 7	$29.95		
Math 6	$29.95		
Math 5	$29.95		
Math 4	$29.95		
Math 3	$29.95		
Subtotal 2			

Total Cost

Subtotal 1

Subtotal 2

Subtotal 3

Cost Subtotal

Shipping and Handling
(Please call for current rates)

G.S.T

Order Total

For students in the following courses, we recommend the corresponding Alberta resources which are highly correlated to the B.C. curriculum.

B.C. Course Name	Corresponding Resource	Price	Quantity	Total
Applications of Math 12	*THE KEY* – Math 30 Applied	$29.95		
	SNAP – Math 30 Applied	$29.95		
Applications of Math 10	**SNAP** – Math 10 Applied	$29.95		
Calculus 12	**SNAP** – Math 31	$29.95		
	Subtotal 3			

Significant discounts for school orders. Prices subject to change.

Please complete the shipping and payment information.
Name: _____
Mailing Address: _____
City: _____ Postal Code: _____
Telephone: _____ School: _____
Visa/MC card number: _____ Expiry Date (mm/yy): _____
Name on Card: _____

ORDERING OPTIONS
On-line: 250.868.8384 or 866.882.8246
Fax: 250.868.9146
E-mail: learnbc@castlerockresearch.com
Mail: #4-1905 Evergreen Court,, Kelowna, BC V1Y 9L4
OR CONTACT YOUR DISTRICT REPRESENTATIVE
(Visit our website for the name of the representative in your area)